D0160521

SUCCESSFUL TECHNICAL WRITING

BOOKS BY TYLER G. HICKS

"Plant Engineer's Easy Problem Solver"
"Pump Selection and Application"
"Pump Operation and Maintenance"
"Successful Technical Writing"

SUCCESSFUL TECHNICAL WRITING

Technical articles, papers, reports, instruction and training manuals, and books

TYLER G. HICKS

Mechanical Engineer; Adjunct Instructor in Mechanical Engineering, Cooper Union School of Engineering (Evening Division); Associate Member, American Society of Mechanical Engineers, American Society of Refrigerating Engineers, and United States Naval Institute; Member, The International Oceanographic Foundation; Editor, "Proceedings" of the Oil and Gas Power Div., ASME

McGRAW-HILL BOOK COMPANY, INC.

New York   Toronto   London   1959

For my eldest son, Greg

PREFACE

This is a practical, hard-hitting book stressing the how-to aspects of technical writing. It is written for every engineer, scientist, technician, and technical writer needing help with his writing. Using the methods given in this book, any technically trained person can improve the quality of his writing. What's more, he'll write faster and easier.

Engineers and scientists write more today than ever before in history. Almost every technical job requires some kind of writing—from the formal report of the results of a research project to the preparation of an instruction manual or technical book. And more and more firms are urging their engineers to write magazine articles and technical papers for publication.

What about these men who must prepare material for publication? Does writing come easy to them—do they obtain maximum output during the time they write? Talk to engineers and scientists and you'll find the answer to both these questions usually is no. This is unfortunate because the writing burden of engineers and scientists is increasing and will continue to increase as long as technology moves forward.

Many solutions to the problem of the increased writing burden are used. Some firms hire huge technical-writing staffs—others farm their writing out to job shops specializing in this work. Advertising agencies form public relations departments to write articles, news, and equipment releases. Hundreds of public relations firms doing little more than technical writing have been spawned in recent years.

But none of these completely relieve the individual engineer and scientist of his obligation to write for the advancement of his field and personal career. In writing for publication, every technically trained man faces the familiar problems writers have tried to solve for hundreds of years—where to get ideas, how to develop them into publishable form, how to outline the writing task, and how to get the job done.

This book offers solutions for most of the writing problems of engineers and scientists preparing material for publication. It covers technical articles, news and equipment releases, engineering and scientific papers, reports, catalogs, advertising, instruction and training manuals, and technical books.

If you want the shortest and surest steps between idea and published manuscript, you'll find them in this book. The procedures given are exact and easy to follow. Though written primarily for engineers, scientists, technicians, and technical writers, many professional writers will also find this book a big help.

Emphasis is placed on how and where to get *good* ideas, and how to develop them into publishable articles, manuals, reports, or books. Every step in the actual writing task is covered—clearly and completely. This is a book that works for and with you. It even tells you how many hours, days, months, or years you'll spend on various writing projects.

To be sure the reader of this book will become completely competent in preparing technical material, much space is also devoted to the word-handling skills he needs. Chapter summaries and exercises are included to help the reader check his grasp of the text.

Many people contributed their know-how to this book. The author is particularly indebted to several members of McGraw-Hill Publishing Company, Inc. The late Phillip W. Swain, formerly chief editor of *Power* magazine, introduced me to the need for clear writing. It was Phil who told engineers "other things being equal, the engineer who writes well will earn $20,000 to $50,000 more during his career than the engineer who can't or won't bother to write well."

Louis N. Rowley, editor and publisher of *Power* magazine, also deserves warm thanks from myself and the many others he taught the complexities of business-magazine editing and writing. James J. O'Connor, managing editor, *Power* magazine, graciously provided the outline for his "Standard Handbook of Lubrication Engineering." Julian Boone, Director of Communications and Publicity, McGraw-Hill Companies, gave me many ideas on writing industrial advertising, as did his excellent book "Industrial Advertising Handbook."

The author is equally indebted to a number of persons in industry, education, engineering societies, and government. They freely gave advice and material.

Lawrence P. Murphy, Jackson Laboratory, E. I. du Pont de Nemours and Company, contributed a large amount of information for Chapter 8. He deserves a major vote of thanks.

Chapter 11, on reports, is partially based on the work of Waldemar A. Ayres, Director of Research and New Product Engineering, White Sewing Machine Company. J. Raleigh Nelson, Professor Emeritus of English, College of Engineering, University of Michigan, contributed the report check list in Chapter 11. This list is probably more widely accepted and used today than any other.

H. C. McDaniel, Manager, Technical Information, Westinghouse Electric Corporation, who did pioneer studies of article leads and whose unique classifications were among the first made available to engineers and scientists, made the excellent analyses which are reflected throughout Chapter 6.

General Electric Company and Ingersoll-Rand Company gave permission to use the quoted material in Chapter 12. The American Society of Mechanical Engineers was extremely generous in releasing data on preparing and presenting technical papers.

The Department of the Air Force, through the efforts of Major James Sunderman, provided much data and material for Chapters 12 and 13. Much of the material contained in Chapter 13 was adapted from four articles—"Let's Improve Our Writing, Not Measure It," "Make a Map to Guide Your Writing," "Illustrate Writing to Help Readers," and "Plan for Continuity in Your Writing"—by Hilary H. Milton, writer and presentations advisor with the Department of the Air Force, and is used with his permission. The Department of the Army and the Department of the Navy are also represented in Chapter 12.

Both these Departments deserve credit equalling that of the Air Force.

The editors of the many business papers quoted, and the authors of the articles in these papers from which examples were taken, contributed their important share to this book. Examples from their articles will serve as excellent guides to every reader of this book.

Hector E. French, Chief, Engineering Publications Department, Sanborn Company, supplied the handy check list in Chapter 12.

William J. Miller, Yarnall-Waring Company, whose foresighted encouragement of engineers and scientists to write is well known in his firm and in many others, was very helpful in connection with Chapter 14.

So you see, this book represents the know-how of a wide cross-section of the technical-writing world. It is my sincere hope that the book will help engineers and scientists everywhere to write better material with less effort.

Tyler G. Hicks

CONTENTS

SUCCESSFUL TECHNICAL WRITING

Chapter 1

WHY WRITE TECHNICAL MATERIAL?

YOU NEVER LOSE

Technical writing always pays off. You never lose when you write a good technical piece. And your payoff can be far beyond your most hopeful dreams. A group of solid articles, an outstanding book, or a few good scientific papers can mean the difference between a routine career and a standout one. Good writing is a sure road to professional recognition.

Every hour you spend writing for publication is packed with opportunity. Good technical material finds its way into print quickly and easily. You profit in at least five different ways (Fig. 1-1) every time you write. How? Let's see.

YOUR RETURNS

The five returns you can usually expect from technical writing are:

1. You contribute knowledge to your field.
2. You help your firm's business.
3. You and your firm gain prestige.
4. You improve your knowledge of the subject.
5. You receive extra income.

Perhaps you can name other returns. If so, fine. But you'll probably find that they fit under one of the five listed here, unless you're a special kind of guy or have an unusual job. Let's take a closer look at these five returns.

BENEFITS TO AUTHORS

professional recognition
and contribution

recognition for you
and your firm

THOUGHT 1   THOUGHT 2   THOUGHT 3

improve your knowledge
and discipline your thinking

personal satisfaction

extra income

Fig. 1-1. Benefits in writing any kind of technical material for publication.
(*Adapted from Westinghouse Electric Corp.*)

You contribute knowledge. Almost every written piece contains something new or different. If you write this kind of material you are definitely contributing something special to your field. All our technology today is the result of many individual contributions. So by adding to the total know-how in your field you help advance technology.

When your contribution is unique—like that of the well-known science and engineering writers—you make a mark that remains for many years. Engineers like Marks, Perry, Terman, Kent, and French made their major contributions through the written word. You can probably name many others who did the same.

There is a real joy that comes to you when you write lasting material. It comes from the realization that you've done more than just pass through the field. You've left something of yourself behind, in written form. Never underrate the importance of contributing know-how. It becomes greater every year you spend in your field.

You help your business. Well-written technical material can help you or your firm's business in several ways. Do a good job when writing new-equipment and news releases and they're more likely to be published. And when published, the better ones will catch the reader's eye.

In articles discussing one type of product you'll probably use your firm's illustrations almost exclusively. This is usual practice. Readers become familiar with what your firm makes, and better business is almost certain to result. But you must watch one angle—don't try to write engineering material solely to bring in more business. Editors will spot you instantly and give you a fast reject.

You gain prestige. Topnotch business papers spend years building up a good editorial reputation. Readers know that the editorial content of the magazines and books published by the leading firms is chosen with the greatest care. Today's readers expect, and get, the best.

So when your by-lined article runs in a leading business paper, both you and your firm share the prestige the magazine has acquired in its field. Never overlook this prestige. A good article, published in a leading magazine, can live for years. During this time it continues to reflect prestige onto the author and his firm. Your name can become a part of the vocabulary of your field.

The same is true, of course, of a good technical book you write. And luckily, the life of a book is longer than an article's. So your prestige lasts longer, and may travel further.

You improve your know-how. Any time you feel you know plenty about your field, sit down and write. You'll discover hundreds of things you've never thought about. Writing about a subject is much like teaching it to others. You must explore your basic reasoning, and this is probably one of the fastest ways to learn more about your subject.

Never try to write for publication unless you're sure of your subject. If you aren't sure, get some good reference books and study them. You'll learn, and at the same time you will get the necessary background for your writing.

A well-written article, book, or other technical piece can, besides increasing your knowledge of the field, be an important milestone in your career. Authors of valuable technical contributions are regarded as peers in their field. Not only do you contribute to the advancement of your chosen occupation—you also engage in a bootstrap operation that can have far-reaching effects on your career and your personal life. Books written early in your career can live throughout your active working life and into your retirement years. Many a book stays in circulation long after the author has left this world.

Earn extra income. Many business papers today pay contributors for original feature articles and for short items suitable for regular features or departments. News releases and new-equipment items are not paid for because these are run for the benefit of both the reader and the contributor.

Most business papers pay their contributors, but some supply reprints or overruns of the article in lieu of money. It is up to you to choose which you prefer.

The rates paid for published material vary considerably from one business paper to another. Some publications base their rates on the column-inch; others pay a flat rate per printed page. Rates range from about $5 to $50 per printed page, depending on the author's standing in the field, the type of article, the editor's need for the material, and the policies of the particular magazine.

Book publishers generally pay their authors on a royalty basis. The author receives a certain percentage of the list or wholesale price of the book, depending on what contractual arrangements have been made. In the typical contract offered by one large publisher, the author receives 10 per cent of the list price of the book on each copy of the first 2,500 copies sold in the U.S., 12.5 per cent on the next 2,500 copies, and 15 per cent thereafter on all copies, including subsequent editions. Sales made through the mail and overseas command lower royalty rates.

That technical writing can produce extra income for you is a proven fact. But the exact amount will vary from one project to another and from one individual to another. For most engineers and technicians the extra income, combined with the other benefits mentioned above, is attractive. But if your only aim is to earn money, technical articles and books will not provide a very lucrative return for the time and energy you spend on them. There must be more than just the money motive behind a given article or book if it is to meet the high standards demanded by today's technical audience.

WHAT YOU MUST GIVE

The benefits of technical writing don't come easy. You must contribute something of yourself to every piece you write. And this takes time, skill, and energy. Throughout this book you'll be learning how to save time and develop skill in your writing. But you must supply the energy and drive yourself (Fig. 1-2).

To write publishable material you must have (1) good ideas, (2) an unbiased approach, and (3) ability to write clearly. Let's see what each of these means.

1. Good ideas. To write in any field you must have new or different ideas about your subject. For in all except the newest fields, many writers have preceded you. Long ago they picked the most obvious topics and worked them over. If you expect to do well in technical writing you must think in terms of the new or different idea, or a new approach to an old idea. It is the approach that gives the personal touch to all the material a good writer turns out.

New ideas you choose must be more than just clever. They must benefit the reader in some way. Only then can you justify the space your story takes. The most successful technical writers today are those who can size up a subject and choose the ideas having the most appeal to the reader. You'll find many ways of doing this discussed

Fig. 1-2. Steps in technical writing. (*Adapted from Westinghouse Electric Corp.*)

in later chapters. And you'll learn where and how to find good ideas for all kinds of technical writing projects.

2. *Unbiased approach.* Of all writing, the technical piece more than any other requires that you strenuously rid yourself of bias. Technical writing is factual writing. So you must stick to your data, results, conclusions, and other information. While there is room for your personal opinions, these must always be guided by the technical aspects of your subject.

One particular bias you must watch very carefully is that which leads you to favor one firm's product over another. Usually the favorite is that built by your own firm. This kind of bias can lead to more editorial rejections than almost any other cause.

3. *Clear writing.* Given a good idea and the right approach, technical writing is little more than clear writing. Anyone who can write a good, clear letter should, with the aid of this book, be able to learn how to write acceptable technical material.

If there is a secret to successful technical writing it can be expressed in one word—simplicity. Throw pomposity and verbosity out of your writing toolbox. They are sure killers of simplicity.

Talk to a hundred editors and you'll find that every one wants one quality above all others in his material—simplicity. Simple writing means high-quality writing. In later chapters you will learn how to keep even the most technical writing simple.

High-quality technical writing almost invariably finds a welcome in some publisher's office. So much of the currently available material is below standard that the staffs of many magazines spend a large part of their time rewriting it. Book publishers frequently find it necessary to hire writers to rewrite manuscripts because while they are excellent from a technical standpoint they are substandard from the writing angle. It is one of the aims of this book to show you ways to overcome the most common writing faults.

When you stop to consider that thousands of manuscripts—articles, books, information and news releases—are rejected every year because of poor quality, you realize that the toll in wasted time and energy is stupendous. You can obviate the possibility of such rejections by keeping two cardinal principles in mind: (1) Be certain that there are several good reasons for writing a piece before you start it; and (2) be certain that every item you turn out is of the highest quality of which you are capable.

WHAT YOU CAN DO

Technical writing is far more powerful than some engineers and scientists realize, or will concede. An outstanding article, paper, or book can reach thousands of people. It can stand for years as the leading item available in its field.

Your writing can spread knowledge of your work, give unusual news, sway or mold opinion. Good writing can make you a force in your field, if you have the technical know-how. You can work for years in relative obscurity, but just publish something and all the others working in your field will quickly rise to agree or disagree with you.

One form of writing can lead to another. Probably the most common path is from a series of articles to a book. You start by writing one or more articles on a subject. They are well received. Editors urge you to do more. Soon you have a group of articles in your file. Someone suggests—or the idea suddenly hits you—that you do a book. Before you realize what has happened, you're writing "Chapter 1" at the top of a page, and starting on a new adventure in your career.

Writing, besides helping you tell others about your work, rounds out your talents. Technical personnel who write well are scarce. By writing some articles, papers, or a book, you train yourself in the art of presenting your ideas clearly and concisely. Such skills are valuable.

Being able to write well can increase your income. If you do a good job of describing your work in print, employers will be more interested in you. And copies of your articles, papers, or book make an excellent presentation when you apply for a promotion or a new job.

WHERE YOU CAN PUBLISH IT

Technical articles usually run in what are today called business papers—magazines covering a specific field or service. Business papers are also called trade journals, technical magazines, and trade papers. Typical business papers are *American Machinist, Textile World, Power, Petroleum Refiner, Heating, Piping and Air Conditioning, Food Engineering,* etc.

There are many ways of classifying business papers. One of the simplest divides them into two categories, horizontal and vertical. Horizontal papers are those that cut across a group of industries, dealing with a service or job function common to them all. Of the six papers mentioned above, *American Machinist, Power,* and *Heating, Piping and Air Conditioning* are of the horizontal type. Each covers a particular subject as applied to a variety of industries. Thus, *American Machinist* deals with metalworking in all industries—from autos to zirconium. Similarly, *Power* covers the generation and application of energy in a wide range of industries, and *Heating, Piping and Air Conditioning* covers these services in the numerous industries that make use of them.

Vertical papers cover a single industry. *Textile World, Petroleum Refiner,* and *Food Engineering* are examples of this type. Though addressed mainly to engineering, managerial, and supervisory personnel, vertical papers can often be profitably read by others in the field. Now what kind of material do horizontal and vertical papers use?

Horizontal papers publish articles dealing with their specialty in any field. *American Machinist* runs articles on metalworking in the auto industry, in electric-motor manufacture, and in turbine construction, as well as probably a hundred others. The key is metalworking, or some other phase covered by the magazine. When you write for this type of paper you must have an idea that applies to the basic field as well as to the particular craft or service.

In a vertical paper, articles generally deal exclusively with the industry served by the publication. Thus, *Textile World* runs articles on the textile industry only. You never expect to see articles on food manufacture in *Textile World;* for these you turn to *Food Engineering.* Before you begin an article for a vertical paper be sure that your material applies to the field covered.

Professional Society Publications. Professional societies like the American Society of Mechanical Engineers, the Institute of Radio Engineers, and the Instrument Society of America have their own publications. These generally publish selected technical papers which have been presented before meetings of the society. So to have your material appear in an engineering or scientific society publication it must usually first be approved for presentation as a technical paper. (See Chapter 10 for a discussion of methods of preparing technical papers.)

Books. When writing a book you have much greater latitude than with articles and papers for the obvious reason that in a book you have more room to examine all phases of a subject. But books, like articles and papers, must meet high editorial standards. And, generally, the better known the book publisher, the higher his standards. The many phases of technical book writing and publishing are discussed in Chapters 15, 16, and 17.

SUMMARY

Technical writing offers you many opportunities for professional development. It can also bring you prestige and greater income while you contribute to the know-how in your field. To succeed in technical writing you must present good ideas in clear language. Your approach must be unbiased. Technical writing is a powerful tool that you can use to advance your field. Depending on the type of material you write, it can be published in business papers, professional society publications, books, and other media.

CHAPTER CHECK-UP

1. What five returns on his efforts can a technical writer usually expect?
2. Describe in detail three aspects of each of these returns.
3. How long can well-written technical material last?
4. What is the range of payment for business papers?
5. Describe a typical contract between a publisher and the writer of a technical book, giving the details of its terms.
6. What must you, as a writer, contribute to any written piece?
7. What are good ideas? How can you judge if your ideas are worthwhile?
8. What bias must you keep in mind whenever you write?
9. Name the most important characteristic of technical writing.
10. What can you accomplish with technical writing?
11. How can one form of writing lead to another?
12. What are the two most common types of business papers?
13. List the characteristics of each of the two major types of business papers.
14. Name two magazines in each of the categories in question 12.
15. What kinds of articles are used in each of the magazines in 14?
16. List the usual characteristics of society publications.
17. What differences will a writer find between writing technical articles, society papers, and technical books?

Chapter 2

TWELVE KINDS
OF TECHNICAL ARTICLES

For our purposes in this book, we'll define a technical article as an organized presentation of facts and data intended to inform, educate, and assist the reader in the performance of his job. Every well-planned technical article has a specific purpose and audience. Once you determine your purpose and your audience, your writing task is simplified because then you can choose the form in which you will present your material.

DIVIDE AND CONQUER

Your first step in learning how to write technical articles is to divide them into their common types, because each type has certain more or less standard elements. Outlines for the various types are given in Chapter 4. It's easy to tackle a particular article when you know its type because you can set it up according to one of these outlines. So let's first take a look at the many forms a technical article can take.

TWELVE KINDS

There are hundreds of different forms in which an article can be presented. But you will find that in most technical magazines the typical contributed article belongs to one of about twelve kinds. The exact number of forms used by a particular magazine varies with its editorial viewpoint, type of handling, and publishing schedule.

The twelve kinds of articles most commonly used in modern business and technical magazines are:

1. Plant descriptions
2. Process descriptions
3. Design procedures
4. Product functions
5. Calculation methods
6. Graphical solutions
7. Operating procedures
8. Maintenance procedures
9. Questions and answers
10. Management techniques
11. Departmental features
12. News and equipment releases

Now let's see what are the characteristics of each kind of article. We'll also give a few examples of each type.

Plant Descriptions. These articles, also called plant stories, describe a particular installation of some kind. The plant-description story usually emphasizes:

A. Plant name and location
B. Details of the equipment
C. What it will do
D. What advantages will result
E. Effect of the plant on business

When the plant is an unusual design, a different procedure is sometimes used. Instead of emphasizing the equipment, the story concentrates on design analyses and related considerations. This gives the reader a better understanding of the problems met with, and how they were solved.

Examples. Descriptions of the installation of a new power plant, petroleum refinery, chemical processing plant, maintenance facility, aircraft factory, air-conditioning system. Note that the plant story can cover an entire plant or a portion of a plant, a new or an established plant, or any other industrial or commercial facility of any kind.

The usual illustrations used in a plant story are:

A. Over-all photo of site and structures
B. Process flow diagram
C. Photos of the equipment
D. Equipment details

Most of the illustrations used in the modern plant story are photos. Drawings are used to show the flow cycle and special design details. With good illustrations, little text is needed. Today some stories consist merely of photos, drawings, and captions.

Choosing photos for plant stories should be done with care. In general, equipment should be clean and neatly painted before it is photographed. But when the photos are to show details of actual construction processes, special painting of the equipment is unnecessary. The workaday appearance of the equipment under these conditions sets a mood for the reader, drawing him into the story.

With more and more attention being given to readability, simplicity in page layout, and better illustrations, the function of photos has changed somewhat. Besides showing the equipment being considered, photos should, if possible, be pleasing to the eye. They should have what editors call "atmosphere." So it is often worthwhile to have photos for plant stories taken by a professional industrial photographer. Effective photos have many uses—in articles, ads, exhibits, records, catalogs, and reports.

Process descriptions. This kind of article tells how a certain process works. It features:

A. Process name and use
B. Raw materials
C. Steps in the process
D. Operating conditions
E. Finished product
F. Rate of output
G. Costs, or savings

Many process descriptions deal with a production-line type of operation. Others cover noncontinuous operations. The requirements for illustrations are similar to those for the plant-story type of article. The process-description type of article is used for a wide variety of products; it applies wherever a material is changed from one form to another.

Examples. Manufacture of chemical products, bottling of foodstuffs, production of textiles, and manufacture of parts by stamping or other machining processes.

Design procedures. This kind of article tells readers how to design a product, plant, or device. It features:

A. Requirements to be met
B. Methods available to meet them
C. Reasons for choosing method described
D. Steps to be followed
E. Special precautions

The design procedures described in technical magazines are often mathematical. But other types are also dealt with. Where the design procedure described is extensive, more than one article may be needed to give all the steps.

Examples. Design of a sleeve bearing, ventilating system, textile weave, bridge, or building.

Illustrations used in the design-procedure article include:

A. Photo of item designed
B. Calculation charts
C. Detail drawings

Product functions. Here you tell the reader how a given product does its job. There is almost an unlimited range of types of products you can cover. Articles of this kind feature:

A. Need for the product
B. How product satisfies the need
C. Reader benefits from product
D. Precautions in using the product

For maximum benefit to your readers, discuss a product in terms of the designs available from several manufacturers. Using data from only one firm is likely to produce a severely limited article or one that appears biased. Editors are inclined to be critical of a limited story.

Of course where the product discussed is the only one built, the article must be limited to it. If any substitutes at all are available, include them briefly, even though they are outdated.

It is extremely important in product-function articles that you keep the reader's interests foremost at all times. Some writers tend to overlook the reader's needs and concentrate on how much space they can devote to glowing descriptions of the product. This is a fatal mistake. No experienced business-paper editor will accept material of this nature until it has undergone major revision to put it into terms that will interest the reader.

Examples. How safety valves work, the use of radio in trucking fleets, high-speed cutting tools for the small shop, and the use of color-fast dyes for nylon fabrics.

Illustrations used in product-function articles include:

A. Photo of product in use
B. Cross section or assembly drawings
C. Installation views (photos)
D. Installation details (drawings or photos)
E. Product details (photos or drawings)

Calculation methods. In this kind of article you show the reader how to compute some value. It is the type of article that vividly appeals to engineers, technicians, and scientists. It features:

A. Value to be computed
B. Factors in the computation
C. Steps to be followed
D. At least one illustrative example
E. Limitations of the method
F. Special precautions

Remember—show a man an easier way to compute something and he'll clip and save your article for years. A well-prepared calculation article is as useful to an engineer as a hammer to a carpenter.

To give the article maximum usefulness, tell the reader exactly what problem is being solved for him. Use a step-by-step procedure from raw data to solution. Present at least one, preferably two, sample problems. When using two problems, be sure to vary the data widely from one to the other. Then the reader can get maximum experience from each.

Where the problem or solution calls for a sketch, use the simplest one possible. The reader of a calculation article usually is eager to learn. The easier you make it for him, the more he will get from your article.

Examples. Calculation of the stresses in special beams, short ways to figure interest rates, fast computation of vehicle operating costs.

Illustrations used in calculation-method articles include:

A. Charts or graphs
B. Photo of item discussed

Graphical solution. The purpose of the graphical-solution article is to present and explain a chart, graph, or other device designed to solve a particular problem. This is a neglected type. It is unfortunate that this is so, because graphical solutions save much valuable time for the user.

A graphical solution can be presented in a number of different forms, including nomograms, intersection charts, tabulations, and two-dimensional plots of data. The objective of all is to save time by helping the user to make a routine calculation with the least effort. Features are:

    A. Statement of the problem
    B. How the chart saves time
    C. Brief description of chart
    D. Equation used in chart
    E. Solution of typical problem
    F. Precautions and limitations

Be extremely careful to choose suitable data ranges for the chart. Thus, if the usual range of actual values is about 10 to 100 and the chart is plotted for 1 to 10, the chart will be almost useless.

Always give the equation on which the chart is based. For the user is lost if he does not know the equation and the units in which it is expressed. Many careful engineers and technicians refuse to use a graphical solution unless they know the equation on which it is based. The only illustrations usually used in this type of article are the charts and sketches needed to solve the problem presented.

Examples. Nomograms for computing various quantities (Fig. 2-1), intersection charts for determining press-fit forces, etc.

Operating procedures. In this kind of article you tell the reader how to run or operate a specific machine or device. To give the reader the widest amount of information, your operating instructions should cover products available from more than one manufacturer. Features are:

    A. Practical approach
    B. Step-by-step procedures
    C. Safety considerations
    D. Routine checks
    E. Operating duties

Operating-procedure articles can be of major assistance to personnel in industries using machinery designed along the lines of that described in the article. A variation of this type of article describes in detail the operating experiences of a new or unique plant. From

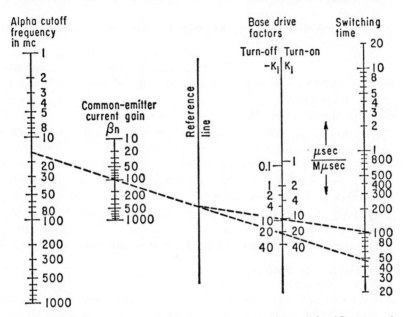

Fig. 2-1. Typical nomogram suitable for use in a magazine article. (*Courtesy of Product Engineering*)

the experiences or conclusions presented, the reader derives information useful on his job, or as general background knowledge.

Examples. Articles on how to operate centrifugal pumps, electric motors, or a trucking fleet. The second type of article might deal with operating experiences in a nuclear-energy power plant, or with snow tires on a fleet of buses.

Illustrations used in articles on operating procedures include:

A. Photo of machine or device
B. Photos of operating procedures
C. Detail drawings of unit
D. Charts of characteristics or limits

Maintenance procedures. In this type of article you tell your readers how to maintain, overhaul, and repair a particular class of equipment. The story features:

A. Strong how-to slant
B. Step-by-step procedures
C. Use of illustrations wherever possible
D. Clear, specific instructions

The secret of success for the maintenance article is the same as for the product-function piece. *The article should be general enough to cover the products of more than one manufacturer.* Only then will you capture a large segment of the readership.

Where a single product is so widely used that many people are interested in its care, the article can logically deal with it alone. But this is relatively rare in industry today.

Examples. Articles on how to maintain diesel engines, textile looms, truck tires, and passenger elevators.

Questions and answers. Here you have a series of questions, each of which is immediately followed by its answer. The questions may cover any subject. Features of a good question-and-answer article are:

A. Short, direct questions
B. Specific answers
C. Covers segment of subject
D. Has beginning, middle, and end

This kind of article is excellent where the reader will have a future use for the material, as in examinations. It's also good where the writer wishes to concentrate his attention on one segment of a subject. By choosing questions dealing only with that segment, he can rid his discussion of useless side issues.

Examples. Questions and answers on pneumatic ash handling, loom overhaul, fuel-injector installation, and refrigeration brine systems. See Fig. 2-2 (page 21) for an excerpt from a typical question-and-answer article.

Management techniques. This kind of article can cover any of a variety of management or business procedures. It often features:

A. One or more case studies
B. Strong personnel slant

C. Specific how-to procedures
D. Emphasis on positive accomplishment
E. Highly practical methods

Management articles are directed to persons in positions ranging from beginners in business to company presidents. The exact level you aim at varies with the publication and the subject matter of the article. Thus an article for shop foremen is written in a different tone from that for general managers.

Illustrations used in the management type of article today include:

A. "Atmosphere" photos
B. Equipment photos
C. Drawings of processes
D. Equipment detail drawings
E. Photos of individuals
F. Reproductions of business forms

The swing today in some management articles is to the personality piece. In this type, an official or outstanding member of a firm forms the core around which the story of the firm is told. These articles are almost always written by a member of the magazine's staff.

Examples. How to get along with your foremen; pay schemes for executives; health problems of refinery workers; how John Doe sparked the ABC Company to its greatest sales record.

Departmental features. Many magazines run regular departments in each issue. Typical departments in which readers can take part are:

A. Letters to the editor
B. Readers' problems
C. Short cuts and kinks
D. Mistakes on the job

The exact names of these departments vary from one publication to another. Thus, *Petroleum Refiner* calls item C "How to Do It"; *Power* magazine calls it "Practical Ideas"; *Chemical Engineering* calls it "The Plant Notebook." All, however, carry similar items— ideas or ways of saving time, money, and effort.

Contributing short items to a department of a magazine is an excellent way for you to start a writing career. The editor gets to

1. What is meant by cetane number of fuel oil?

A. Cetane scale is applied to fuel oils, gasoline, diesel fuel, etc., to show oil's ignition quality. This quality means oil's ability to ignite in diesel cylinder—or under similar conditions. Fuel with good ignition quality will auto-ignite at low temperatures and is, therefore, preferred. This quality affects engine starting, smoking, and knocking.

Hydrocarbon family ranges from simple combinations, such as methane gas, through various solids, liquids, and gases. Some have complicated chemical structures. All have various ignition characteristics. Formula for cetane is $C_{16}H_{34}$.

Cetane is an excellent diesel fuel in its pure form, but isn't easy to separate completely from other hydrocarbons. Cetane content for various crudes differs greatly. $C_{10}H_7CH_3$ is another hydrocarbon, but it has poor ignition qualities. Cetane number is based on proportions of these two hydrocarbons.

Cetane number of 100 means ignition quality equal to pure cetane, while zero means one equal to that of alpha-methyl-naphthalene ($C_{10}H_7CH_3$). Ignition number of 60 means mixture equivalent to one composed of 60% cetane and 40% $C_{10}H_7CH_3$.

2. What is meant by right- and left-hand engines? Buyers ordering two engines for same plant often specify one each. Is this good practice?

A. Engine is classified as right or left when flywheel is on right or left sides, viewing engine from operating side. Reason one engine of each is specified is because owners believe such an arrangement is easier to attend if controls are on same aisle between engines.

Diesel Engine Manufacturers Association says there may have been reason for such an arrangement years ago before the days of remote governor control, but not with today's common use of such control and the little attention modern engines need.

Such specifications require one engine to be nonstandard. Disadvantage to owner is loss of interchangeability, which is so important to avoid carrying large stocks of spare parts. Then, again, any advantage is lost if a third diesel is installed.

know your material. If it's good, he'll be happy to consider any longer pieces you do. Also, you can learn a lot by comparing your original copy with the edited version that runs in the magazine.

Before you contribute anything, study the entire magazine, particularly the department, for several issues. This will give you a feel for the level, writing style, length, and general approach the editor prefers.

For best results when submitting departmental material, try to follow these four pointers:

1. Keep the text short, and to the point.
2. Use a photo or sketch if possible.
3. Keep your explanations simple.
4. Give step-by-step procedures, if possible.

3. If engine fails to start, what would you look for?

A. Engine rarely fails to start, but such difficulty can be divided into two groups: (1) Starting mechanism fails to turn engine through an operating cycle. (2) Engine turns through operating cycle but fails to fire. If starting mechanism doesn't work, check starting air pressure or look for run-down or weak battery—depending on starting system.

If air-starting pressure is high enough, air-starting valves may not open fully or at right time. Or by sticking, leaky exhaust or inlet valves may prevent engine from quickly raising compression high enough to fire. Leakage from stuck rings or badly grooved cylinders may have same effect. In cold weather, heat of compression may be too low unless cooling water and (in extreme cases) even lube oil are heated.

At times, bearings are too tight (after overhaul) or there is no lubrication on cylinder walls, etc. All this puts extra load on starting mechanism.

Fig. 2-2. Three typical questions and answers from a published article (*Courtesy of Power*)

Examples. How to magnetize a screwdriver, clamps to hold a hammer in a tool chest, short calculation for partial pressures, six steps in drawing a fan scroll casing.

News releases. Many magazines divide news items into three categories:

1. Industry news
2. New-equipment items
3. Personnel changes

Industry news items: These cover the big and small stories of interest to people in the field covered by the magazine. The test question for such items is: Will they interest a large segment of the people in the industry? If the answer is yes, an item has a good chance of being published. *Examples.* Changes in laws governing the industry operations, late data on and prices of raw materials, details of new or unusual plants, important technical developments, new practices used abroad.

New-equipment items: These are run for the benefit of all readers of a magazine. To get best results from the new-equipment item:

1. Keep the item short and concise.
2. Furnish a good photo or drawing with the text.
3. *Always* give the capacity, size, materials and other pertinent details of the product.
4. *Never* knock a competitor's product.
5. *Don't submit* the item unless the unit is really new.
6. Omit all unnecessary information.

1. Do not submit new-equipment items longer than one double-spaced typewritten page. Unless your unit will revolutionize the

For more data on these items, use post cards p 175. Identify your request with item number.

Wet-dust collectors

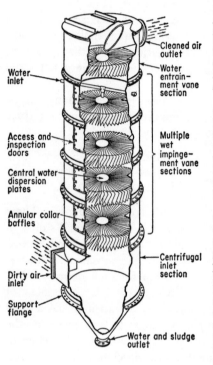

1023 · Centrifugal wet-dust collector, *Type CW-1*, solves dust-control problems that cloth-type collectors cannot handle. These problems include high temperature or moisture; explosive or combustible dusts; corrosive, highly abrasive, or obnoxious dusts; or a combination of the foregoing.

Collector is of counter-current design and of tower-type construction. It consists of multiple wet-vane sections and a final water entrainment vane section. Diameter of collector varies in proportion to air volume handled and number of wet-vane sections is governed by application requirements.

Water supply enters above top wet-vane section and flows downward or counter to upward flowing air, which enters collector through the lower tangential inlet. Patented vane is said to provide increased impingement surface and impart centrifugal action to both air and water to produce thorough intermixing. Water and dust are discharged as sludge from lower cone and clean air from air outlet at top. After clarification in settling tanks, water may be recirculated since no spray nozzles are used, the water inlet being an open-end pipe.

Pangborn Corp, Hagerstown, Md.

field, items longer than this are a waste of time. Study the magazines. Note that almost all the items run about 15 lines on a 12- or 13-pica measure. So be concise. Use simple language. Editors will love you for it. And if they want more information, they'll be knocking on your door sooner than you think.

2. Try to submit a *good* photo or drawing with every release. You tell a better story, and the reader gets the point sooner. Compare the items in Fig. 2-3. Note how much better the illustrated item tells its story. Your eye flicks from the illustration to the text and back again, giving you the complete idea.

Anti-seize thread compound

1042 · Thread compound is said to eliminate seizing and galling at operating temperatures to 1200 F. Called *Thred-Gard*, it is nonhardening and acts as a lubricant to allow easy disassembly of threaded connections. Compound also prevents damage to stud, bolt, pipe-joint and plug threads. By reducing wrench torque, *Thred-Gard* allows fitting to be drawn tighter without undue stress or strain. It acts as protective coating to keep threaded surfaces smooth and insure pressure-tight, metal-to-metal contact, according to manufacturer.

Crane Packing Co., Dept PRN, 1800 Cuyler Ave, Chicago 13, Ill.

Low-toxicity solvent

1071 · *Vythene*, low-toxicity safety solvent, is only 1/20 as toxic as carbon tetrachloride. Solvent is nonflammable, fast evaporating and suitable for a variety of industrial uses. It may be used for cleaning electric motors and equipment, plant maintenance, wax dispersion or removal, cleaning machinery.

Showing excellent stability for all metals including aluminum, brass, and copper, even at the boiling point of the solvent, *Vythene* is noncorrosive to brass and copper and practically inert to ordinary electrical insulating varnish and materials.

Tect, Inc., Cortlandt and Erie Sts., Dumont, N.J.

Fig. 2-3. Three typical new-equipment items. Note how the illustration improves the usefulness of an item. (*Courtesy of Power*)

Unless your product is extraordinary, don't submit more than two or three illustrations with it. Supplying more is wasteful because rarely is more than one illustration used to show the unit. The purpose behind supplying two or three is to give the editor a choice of illustrations without overburdening your budget.

3. Be certain to give the capacity, size, applications, materials, and other pertinent data about the unit. Remember, many readers of new-equipment items are looking for units to solve a specific problem. Unless you give readers the major details about a device, they cannot tell if it is suitable. And experience shows that many busy men will not stop to inquire further unless the data show that there's a good chance that the device is suitable.

So think before you write. List all the important data about a unit. Get this information and include it in the first paragraph of your release. Figures 2-3 is a good example of this procedure.

4. Never knock competitors' products in your release. It takes up space you could use for your own product. And no editor wants to see the other guy knocked, regardless of his personal feelings or beliefs about the product.

5. New-equipment columns are for *new* products. If you paint a pump green instead of brown, don't write a release about it. The

product must be new—either a completely new design or an up-dated design involving extensive changes. Such small items as changing a handle or redesigning a base are types of alterations that do not rate the space for a new-equipment release. Submitting material like this only makes the editor's job tougher. So limit your write-ups to the real thing.

6. If the president of your firm introduces a new product at a picnic with every salesman and distributor present—fine—but don't include this in your release. It's unnecessary information. Space in new-equipment columns is limited, and you'll have enough trouble cutting the pertinent data down to size. Stick to the product and its important characteristics in your releases. Address your release to the New Products Editor and include the full name and address of your firm.

Personnel changes: These releases (including obituaries) should be kept short and to the point. Where your release concerns a promotion, transfer, or change in assignment, give both the new and the old position and title of the individual. Do not give his complete career history unless he is being advanced to a really important position— chairman of the board, member of the board, president, executive vice-president, vice president. For other positions, there generally is not enough space to give complete career details. But to be sure, study the magazine. There is some variation from one paper to another.

In obituaries, give the person's age, date and place of death, title and position, and a short summary of his career. If he made significant contributions to his field, these should be stated. Survivors are usually listed last. If one or more survivors are active in the same field as the deceased, give a short summary of their activities.

EXAMPLES OF ARTICLE TYPES

Listed below are 36 magazines that feature good examples of each of the twelve types of articles we discussed above. Note several items about this list. The magazines listed are by no means the only publications running representative articles of the various types. They do, however, run excellent examples of one or more types of articles. Actual article titles and page numbers are not given, as they would soon be outdated. Styles in magazines, like women's fashions, are constantly changing. The vogue today may be shunned tomorrow. Be careful to note that some business papers use little or no contributed material. The magazines listed use predominantly contributed material.

So use the list below carefully. You can find copies of the magazines in most large libraries, or you can purchase them from the main or branch offices of the publisher, from large news dealers, or from back-issue stores. If one of the magazines strongly appeals to you, subscribe to it for a year or more. There is no better way to get to know the preferences of an editorial staff than reading every issue for a year or more. (Note that many business papers today have rather stringent requirements that potential subscribers must meet.)

For typical examples of the twelve types of articles discussed earlier in this chapter, refer to the following magazines:

1. Plant descriptions
   Power
   Textile World
   Public Works Magazine

2. Process descriptions
   Petroleum Refiner
   Food Engineering
   Engineering and Mining Journal

3. Design procedures
   Product Engineering
   Heating, Piping and Air Conditioning
   Engineering News-Record

4. Product functions
   Fleet Owner
   American Machinist
   Marine Engineering

5. Calculation methods
   Electronics
   Control Engineering
   Design News

6. Graphical solutions
   Chemical Engineering
   Machine Design
   Air Conditioning, Heating and Ventilating

7. Operating procedures
   World Oil
   Coal Age
   The Welding Engineer

8. Maintenance procedures
   Electrical Construction and Maintenance
   Butane-Propane News
   Mill and Factory

9. Questions and answers
   Industrial Refrigeration
   Industrial Distribution
   Electrical Merchandising

10. Management techniques
    Factory Management and Maintenance
    Petroleum Engineer
    Electrical World

11. Departmental features
    Power Engineering
    Oil and Gas Journal
    Machinery

12. News releases
    Purchasing
    Aviation Week
    Electrical Engineering

SUMMARY

Your best guide to understanding the kinds of articles used in business papers today is to classify them by type. Most contributed articles fall into one or more of about twelve common forms. Each form has certain general characteristics. Certain types of illustrations are popular for each article form.

An excellent way to start a part-time writing career is to contribute short items to a magazine's departments. Study a magazine before submitting material to it. Subscribe, if you are sincerely interested in the field.

CHAPTER CHECK-UP

1. Name the twelve common types of technical articles.
2. List typical characteristics of each of the twelve types.
3. Give two examples of each type of article.
4. What is one good way of securing photos for an article?
5. From six business papers of your choice, choose examples of ten different article types.
6. What are the characteristics of news items?
7. Choose a typical published new-equipment item and point out its characteristics.
8. Name three types of personnel notices. What does each type feature?
9. Study twelve business papers and list three kinds of articles used in each paper.

Chapter 3

HOW TO FIND AND DEVELOP ARTICLE IDEAS

IDEAS ARE EVERYWHERE

Look around you today. Article ideas are everywhere. All you need do to latch onto a few is train yourself to think in the right terms. Scientific personnel, engineers, and technicians are particularly fortunate. For them, article ideas can be found so quickly they'll never have time to put them all to use.

LOOK AT YOUR JOB

Try to remember the day you started on your present job. Remember how new everything seemed? When some procedure was explained, you followed it step by step, classifying each task. Now, probably, all the procedures seem second nature. You know them so well that you hardly have to think about them.

But what about a newcomer to your job? He'd see your duties in much the same light as you did those first few days. Focus your thoughts on those early days and list the steps in some of the procedures you learned. Show such a list to a new man and watch his eyes glow. Why? You've relieved him of thinking through the steps. You've saved him time and energy, and made life a bit easier for him. This is the intent of almost every article run in the business press today. You must help or inform the reader in some way—if you don't, forget your article.

So look at your job and your duties. There's a wealth of article material in both. But don't stop there. If you're taking a course, or studying some subject on your own, stand back and take another look. What phase was especially tough? Now that you understand it, can you give a better explanation? If so, you probably have a good idea for an article.

LIST YOUR IDEAS

If your job presented no new problems, then take another tack. Write your job title on a piece of paper. What is it? Design engineer, laboratory mechanic, machine operator? In these three titles there should be at least eighteen article ideas. Let's find a few of them.

Assume you're a design engineer. What do you design? We'll say it's mobile radar units. How do you design them? Stop right there. That's your first article idea—*how to design mobile radar units*.

Now think some more. What happens when you design a unit? You run into problems—probably hundreds of them. The story of how any of these are solved would probably be a good article. So include some of your toughest problems in the list.

Once the unit is designed, it must be built. And what happens? More problems. The same is true for operation and maintenance. Now let's see how many article ideas we've found. List them like this:

1. How to design mobile radar units
2. Humidity problems in mobile radar sets
3. Weight problems in mobile radar sets
4. Circuitry problems in mobile radar sets
5. Assembly procedures for mobile radar sets
6. Operation and maintenance of mobile radar sets

This list is just a beginning. Item 1, design, could include the design of every one of the many parts of the set as well as of the set as a whole. The construction problems—items 2, 3, and 4—could be expanded almost indefinitely. Ask any design engineer. He'll bend your ear for hours.

Item 5, manufacture, could deal first with the actual set. After you'd written a few articles on this phase, you could switch to the production machines and techniques for assembling the sets. This subject should provide material for at least two articles. Much the same is true of item 6.

So if you really want to write technical articles, start an idea file. List every idea that comes to you. Take pencil in hand a few times and build ideas from a job title, a responsibility, or any other subject. Soon ideas will be coming to you when you least expect them. Jot them down immediately and toss the list into a folder. Work this scheme for a few weeks and you'll have a sizable file.

TESTED METHODS FOR PRODUCING IDEAS

Here are nine ways to produce ideas. All have worked for writers of technical articles. Try each one. Choose those that work best for you and concentrate on them in the future.

1. Ask your associates what their technical problems are, and how they solve them.
2. Study the articles and ads in the magazines in your field.
3. Expand your know-how of a subject.
4. Survey a field, and summarize its literature.
5. Check with your firm's public relations director or agency.
6. Study the handbooks in your field.
7. Look for photo and sketch subjects.
8. Watch for graphical ways to solve problems.
9. Ask your associates what subjects they think need discussion in articles.

Let's take a quick look at each method to see how to use it. Remember, you can alter any technique to suit your needs.

Ask your associates. Concentrate on people in the same field as your own. Then you'll have a good understanding of most of their problems. First ask, "What is your worst problem?"

Listen carefully to the answer. If the method used to solve the problem is different in one or more aspects from usual procedures, you probably have an article idea. Your associate, in most cases, will be willing to give you the complete details for use in an article, or he will become a coauthor with you.

Study the magazines. Read the outstanding business papers in your field. Go through the magazines from cover to cover. Study both the articles and the ads. Some articles may tell only part of a story that you know well. If so, check with the editor (see Chapter 5) about doing another piece from a different viewpoint.

Other articles may suggest new ideas to you. An article on pumps may make you wonder if anything has been done on piping for these pumps. Check. If not, you're the man to do the piping article.

Ads are a fine source of article ideas. For almost every advertised product interests the readers of the magazine. And the more ads about a given type of product, the greater the interest. Reading the ads also broadens your knowledge of the firms in the field, their latest products, and the information available about them. All this is valuable background for your writing.

Expand your know-how. Is there a phase of your work you should know better? If so, why not take some courses or do some specialized study of this phase? Courses and research, coupled with your previous education and experience, can give you a valuable knowledge of your field. They may even give you enough know-how to write some articles.

Watch out for too little knowledge when using this method. Editors spot shallow articles almost immediately. So get a good, solid background of information before you sit down to write. Then you will be almost certain of finding a publisher for your material.

Survey a field. If you're interested in a field related to your own, make a careful survey of it. Review its major statistics, the firms doing business in it, the literature available, the outstanding personnel, and its history. A survey should give you many article ideas. Even if it doesn't, you can almost always use the literature summary as an article. Be sure your summary is up-to-date and includes the important contributions to the field.

Check with public relations. If you work for a large firm, chances are there's a public relations man on the payroll. Get to know him. He's probably hungry to meet personnel interested in writing technical material. He may have so many ideas for articles that he'll keep you busy for years. Follow your PR man's recommendations. He usually has had long experience and knows what editors need.

Smaller firms, and some large ones, may use a public relations agency, or an ad agency having a PR department. If this applies to your firm, contact the agency. The man handling your account is certain to have some article ideas and to know editors' needs, if he's worth his fee. Work with PR or ad agencies in the same way that you would with your own PR department.

Study handbooks. Well-written engineering, scientific, and business handbooks are excellent idea sources for alert writers. Pick up a handbook on your field and see for yourself. Read a few of the sections. Note how each summarizes its subject.

If your mind is receptive to article ideas, you'll find that certain key words suggest topics. In a section covering railroad track, the details about switches may suggest a product-function type of article surveying the various kinds of switch operators. Or a section on purchasing may give you a lead to an operating-procedure article on the purchase of specialized equipment—searchlights, bus horns, snow tires, etc.

Search for picture stories. Get yourself a good camera, or line up a few good industrial photographers. Then search your job and plant for picture stories. Look for any step-by-step operation that's important in your business. This is almost certain to be of interest to readers. But before taking any photos, check your idea with some editors. See Chapter 5 for the tips on querying editors.

If you don't have a camera, or the story doesn't lend itself to photos, try sketches. Get a pad of unruled paper and make a simple, clear sketch of each step. Write a caption for each sketch, then perhaps a short, general statement about the problem or process. Query an editor.

Watch for graphical solutions. Many firms prepare charts, slide rules, schedule boards, and other devices to make routine jobs easier. Some of these are excellent subjects for graphical-solution articles or short departmental features.

Make a list of the graphical solutions available. Find out if you would be allowed to publicize them. If so, contact an editor. When you develop a graphical solution yourself, you need not get company permission to publish it unless the firm has specific rules regarding writing. But play it safe and get permission anyway.

Ask your friends. Check with your associates; ask them "What article do you think would do most good for our field today?" You'll be amazed to see how many excellent article ideas pop up. You probably won't be able to do an article on every idea suggested. But there will be plenty that you're qualified to do.

This scheme has the advantage of timeliness. The ideas you're given are those that are important at the moment. And every good

business-paper editor loves these. They help him give better and
hotter news to his readers.

CLASSIFY YOUR IDEAS

Once your ideas begin to roll in, they'll give you trouble unless
you classify them. Classifying your ideas is the first step toward successful technical writing. For unless you classify you're lost—smoth-
ered with ideas that uselessly float around your mind. Follow these
four steps to classify your ideas:

1. Write the idea on paper as soon as it hits you.
2. Toss the paper into a special general-idea folder.
3. When you have time, review your ideas.
4. Put each idea into a suitable folder or file.

These steps make it easy for anyone to get a good start on classifying
his article ideas.

Step 1. You can't classify ideas unless you can remember them.
And if you're the typical technical writer, you'll remember only your
poor ideas. The good ones flash through your mind and disappear,
unless you write them down. So play safe. Write down every idea as
soon as it hits you. This is the only way to hook those big ones and
get them permanently on paper. Besides, once you've written down
an idea you can forget it and turn to looking for new ones.

Step 2. Toss your ideas into a general-idea folder. Once you begin
to write and get your material published, you'll start to think of this
folder as a bank. For it will contain the principal on which you will
draw for much of your future writing.

Allowing an idea to rest in a general folder for a few days or weeks
has advantages. Ideas seem to season or grow stale, depending on
whether they're good or bad. Coming on an idea cold allows you
to judge it better. This way you're more likely to scrap the poor ones
and save the good ones.

Step 3. Take time out to review your ideas at regular intervals.
Close your office door and tell your secretary you want some quiet.
Go over the ideas quickly. Toss out those that sound trite or would
require more effort than you can expend. Don't keep poor ideas
around—they have a way of spoiling your good ones, sooner than
you think. Not only that, you waste time whenever you review a poor

idea after you've decided it's no good. Put your good ideas into a neat pile before classifying them.

Step 4. Set up a twelve-folder file. Label each folder with one of the article types listed in Chapter 2. Now take your article ideas, and with only one to a slip of paper, toss each into the correct folder. If you're in doubt about an idea because it could fit into more than one category, put it into the folder in which it seems to have the greatest use.

If you write only a few articles a year, say six or less, file folders are good for classifying your ideas. But if you write a large number of articles it's better to organize your materials more extensively. Here's one way that works well for many technical writers.

Classification form. Figure 3-1 shows a typical form useful for organizing article ideas after they've been classified. Prepare a form on 8½- by 11-in. paper for each of the twelve article types listed in Chapter 2. Use punched paper so that the forms can be kept in a ring binder.

Divide the paper into seven vertical columns and enter the headings shown for each, from left to right: (1) Idea, (2) Date entered, (3) Work needed before writing, (4) Publication possibilities, (5) Date

ARTICLE TYPE: PLANT DESCRIPTIONS						
(1) IDEA	(2) DATE ENTERED	(3) WORK NEEDED BEFORE WRITING	(4) PUBLICATION POSSIBILITIES	(5) DATE WRITING STARTED	(6) DATE WRITING FINISHED	(7) PUBLICATION DETAILS
New Line Diesel Power Plants	1/15/59	Get two photos: (1) Exterior view (2) Interior view. Get plot plan from Air Force	Power Power Engineering Consulting Engineer Diesel Power	5/1/59	6/29/59	Published in Power 12/59; article length two pages; reprints ordered
New Pumping Station for Textile Mill	5/17/59	Get plans from the consulting engineer; read all job specs; write pump builder for photos	Textile World Cotton Digest Southern Textile News Textile Industries	8/10/59	9/30/59	Returned by Textile World 10/28/59; sent to Cotton Digest 11/3/59. Accepted 12/15/59. To be published 3/60.

Fig. 3-1. Form for recording article ideas. You can alter this form to suit your needs.

writing started, (6) Date writing finished, and (7) Publication details.

Under heading 1 list the idea as taken from the folder. Be sure to give enough data so that you can recall the exact story in the future. Enter the date the idea is listed on the form. This will be close to the date you originally got the idea, if you review your ideas regularly. If you don't, then put the date on the paper when you first make a note of the article idea.

Be sure to keep the various dates relating to an article—when you first had the idea for it (column 2), when you started writing, and when you finished. Why? Well, if you write regularly you'll begin to spot a pattern to the development of an article. Once you reach this stage in your writing, the ideas will come easier, the words will flow smoothly, and you'll produce at least twice as much as when you started. Dates also help you see when an article has been around too long, and when you need a little prodding to reduce your backlog of ideas.

Column 3 tells you what to do before starting to write. If photos or drawings are needed, make a note in this column. And get all these materials before you start the text. There's nothing quite so disappointing or wasteful as to write an article and then find that the key illustrations are not available.

List in column 4, in the order of preference, the business papers for which you think the article is suited. Then you can direct your writing better.

Insert your starting and completion dates in columns 5 and 6. Enter publication details—the name of the paper and the date on which the article appeared—in column 7.

The form in Figure 3-1 is not the only one you can use. Alter it to suit your particular needs. Avoid the use of complex forms. The longer it takes to fill out a form, the less time you have for writing. Complex forms just give you one more excuse for not writing. And goodness knows, there are enough of these now. So why invent another?

MAKE YOUR IDEAS BLOSSOM

Though it sounds old-fashioned, every article must have a beginning, a middle, and an end. This is true whether the piece is long or short. Once you sense the need for these three elements, your articles will become better balanced and more professional in their make-up.

To develop your ideas so that they have a beginning, middle, and end takes skill and experience. One method that works well for many technical writers resembles brainstorming. You might call it "randomizing." To use it, do the following:

1. Write the article idea at the top of a piece of paper.
2. Under the idea list every word or short group of words related to the idea that you can think of.
3. Don't attempt to edit or arrange the words in any specific order; simply list them as they occur to you.
4. Think of the article idea from as many different angles as possible—from the viewpoint of the general reader, or a mechanic working on the equipment, of an engineer designing it, etc.; continue listing words that occur to you.
5. Read as many related articles and books on your subject as you can; continue listing words.
6. Review your list of words and phrases and arrange them in a rough outline form—under Beginning, Middle, and End.
7. Mark those ideas which will be illustrated, noting the type of illustration to be used—photo or drawing.

Now let's take a look at how this method might be applied to a specific article idea. To make the example as useful as possible we'll choose a fairly common type of article—a plant description of a new machine shop. Make your idea blossom by first listing words at random like this:

AB Company's New Machine Shop

Work flow	Locker room	When started
Type of work handled	Shapers	When finished
Machine tools	Lathes	Output expected
Personnel	Drill presses	Materials handling
Reasons for new plant	Disposal of old ma-	Aims in plant design
Designers and builders	chines	Construction troubles
Where located	Safety considerations	Type of building
	Size	

There are twenty-one random ideas here. They've all grown from the simple article idea under which they are listed. One interesting and important aspect of this method is that when you list your ideas, they're all related to a single article. Other methods sometimes allow unrelated ideas to creep in, complicating your job. Now let's rearrange these ideas so they roughly fall into a beginning, middle, and end.

Beginning	*Middle*	*End*
Where located	Machine tools	Aims in plant design
Size	Shapers	Designers and builders
When started	Lathes	
When finished	Drill presses	
Type of work handled	Personnel	
Reasons for new plant	Locker room	
Work flow	Safety considerations	
Type of building	Materials handling	
Output expected	Disposal of old machines	
	Construction troubles	

With this general arrangement of your article you are now ready to prepare a formal outline. But before sitting down to do the outline, take care of one more detail—permission to do the story.

GET PERMISSION

If your article is based on data from your firm, check with your supervisors to see that they approve the use of the material. There's no point to writing an article and then having it killed by management. When using data relating to government defense work, be certain to secure a written release from the appropriate agency or department.

Some firms are extremely cautious when it comes to releasing material concerning their work. So play it safe. Always get permission to use the material and illustrations that will go into the article. Then there's relatively little danger that you'll have to scrap the article later. Killing an article after it is in type is an expensive and painful ordeal for the author, his firm, and the editors. The best way to avoid this kind of unpleasantness is to get permission from the proper authorities in your firm and from all sources supplying you data and illustrations. *Always get permission—start now. Never submit an article unless you have full permission to use the material.*

SUMMARY

Train yourself to be on the lookout for article ideas every day on your job. You're certain to find some excellent ideas that never occurred to you before. Practice with one or more of the other methods given in this chapter to produce article ideas. Classify your ideas at regular intervals, discarding all the poor ones. Set up a form to help you keep track of your ideas. Before starting an article, work over your idea so it blossoms into a complete story having a beginning, a middle, and an end. Never start an article until you are certain that your firm and supervisors approve of the subject, its handling, and the illustrations you will use. Also secure approval from any other firms, agencies, or authors whose material you will use.

CHAPTER CHECK-UP

1. Name twelve ways to obtain article ideas.
2. Develop six article ideas from your job title.
3. How can your friends help you get article ideas?
4. Look through a business paper of your choice and develop three article ideas from it.
5. List three subjects you're interested in learning more about. Choose one and develop six article ideas from it.
6. List three fields you'd like to survey. Choose one and develop six article ideas about it.
7. How can you work with public relations people to develop ideas?
8. How can step-by-step processes be presented in articles?
9. What four steps should you follow when classifying your ideas?
10. Sketch a typical classification form for your article ideas and explain its use.
11. What is the most common characteristic of good technical articles?
12. List the seven steps in developing article ideas.
13. Choose an article idea and show how each step in question 12 is carried out.
14. When should you secure permission to use material and illustrations in an article?

Chapter 4

HOW TO OUTLINE AN ARTICLE

WHY OUTLINE?

There are many arguments for preparing an outline for every article you write. Here are seven good reasons:

1. To help you analyze your ideas about the subject
2. To give continuity to your story
3. To prevent omission of important points
4. To help you decide on the best method for telling your story
5. To ensure a beginning, middle, and end for your story
6. To help you tailor your story to the editor's needs
7. To allow you to concentrate on the writing of the story

Let's take a quick look at each of these reasons.

Analyze your ideas. If you don't plan your article before you start writing, you're certain to run into trouble. So analyze your ideas before writing. And the easiest way to do this is to list, at random, all your ideas about a subject, as we did in Chapter 3. Once you have your ideas on paper, you can concentrate on arranging them in a suitable order for the type of article you have in mind. Later in this chapter you'll find a number of typical outlines for articles of various kinds.

Give your story continuity. A well-organized story reads smoothly because the writer has analyzed his ideas and arranged them logically. And continuity is one of the surest bench marks of the experienced technical writer. If your aim is to captivate an editor, then strive for continuity. How? Outline before you write.

Don't omit important items. Careless planning is a sure way to overlook important parts of your subject. Usually, you won't remember these until the article is nearly finished. Then you will have to go back, rewrite, insert new paragraphs, and try to connect to the existing material. This seldom works. You wind up with a jerky, disconnected story that jars the reader's mind. And since editors are probably the most sensitive readers in the world, you're certain to spoil their day. So, above all, outline before you write.

Choose your story form. While making your outline you must review all your text and illustration material. When you do this, a pattern for telling your story will emerge. You'll find that your materials lend themselves best to one of several types of presentations—a picture story, a question-and-answer scheme, a text story with only a few illustrations, or a graphical-solution story with one or more illustrations and relatively little text. Once you know the story form you wish to use, it is easier to set up your outline.

Every article has three parts. Your outline ensures your having a beginning, middle, and end for your article, as discussed in Chapter 3. Developing and planning these three parts give your article continuity. And remember—it's the smooth story based on a good idea that wins the editor's approval.

Tailor your article. When you write on assignment, as you will once editors get to know you and your work, you must tailor-make your articles. And the easiest way to do this is to make an outline before writing.

Help yourself concentrate. Your biggest advantage when you make an outline is the freedom your mind enjoys while you write the article. Why? For several reasons. Once you outline your article and know that you've covered all the important points, you can forget every item except the one you're writing about. This allows you to concentrate fully on every word, sentence, and paragraph. There's no danger of starting with facts that should be in the middle of your story instead of at the beginning, so you don't have to worry.

Do some technical writers work without outlines? Can an article be written without an outline? The answer to both these is yes. But the writer who works without an outline sweats more and produces less copy. His articles lack continuity; they are likely to be uneven in style, illogically arranged, and poorly written. Outlines won't solve every problem you run into when writing an article. But they will make your writing life much easier and ensure better results.

STEPS IN OUTLINING AN ARTICLE

There are three basic steps in outlining any technical article:

1. Assemble all your facts.
2. Collect all your illustrations.
3. Classify your facts and illustrations.

Let's see how you can best perform each step.

1. Assemble your facts. For your first few outlines, and for difficult articles, use the methods given in Chapter 3 to develop an idea. But once you've gained some experience, you can work more directly. To do this, set up three columns on a sheet of paper. As in Chapter 3, the first column should list items for the beginning of the article, the second for the middle, the third for the end.

Under each heading insert key words for the important topics you intend to cover. If you have your order firmly in mind, you can insert these key words in the exact sequence you expect to use them in the article. Then you'll be ready to transfer the key words from this rough outline to your finished outline.

2. Assemble your illustrations. Secure all the illustrations you intend to use in your article. Don't start the outline until you have every illustration you need. Key drawings or photos can make or break a technical article. If you cannot obtain good illustrations you might as well not write the article, unless the editor plans to supply them. (See Chapter 5.)

Some writers start to secure their illustrations immediately after deciding to write an article. This is often long before they start producing copy. So while working on other stories they keep tabs on the material rolling in for future articles. This makes sense because it usually takes from several weeks to a month or more to obtain illustrations from various sources.

3. Classify facts and illustrations. Put your facts where they belong in the story. Don't drop them in at random as you write. Smooth writing comes from good outlining. But what goes where in your outline and story? Let's see.

THE LEAD

Your lead for a technical article should contain answers to three questions: What is this article about? Why should it be read? How will the reader benefit from it?

The answers may not always be given directly—some parts may be implied. But by answering all parts of these questions you summarize the article for the reader. And the summary type of lead is preferred by many editors today, even though you see other types of leads used.

Summarizing your article in the lead paragraph helps the reader decide if he must read your entire story. You save his time. And both he and the editor will love you for it. So remember—what, why, how. See Chapter 6 for instructions on writing a snappy lead.

THE MIDDLE

Here's where you give the solid facts to your reader. You answer, in a detailed way, the three questions posed in your lead. Tell your reader what the equipment, procedures, or other items do, give, or produce, or how they help. Don't skimp on facts. But don't go back to the beginning of time to start your explanations.

Know what kind of a reader you're writing for. Keep him in mind. If he's a mechanic, see that your ideas stick to his needs—tools, how they're used, how job methods are improved. But if your reader is an engineer or scientist, direct your words at design, performance, tests, management procedures. See Chapter 7 for the ways to keep the middle lean and strong.

THE END

Summarize your results and stop. Show what your story means for the future and stop. Don't drag out your ending. You'll lose your reader.

One paragraph is often enough for ending a technical article. Some editors avoid any formal ending. When the story finishes presenting all the pertinent facts, it ends. Reading this type of article gives you the feeling that its tail was chopped off. But it saves space. And that's why it's used.

But play it safe. Use a one-paragraph ending. It's easier for the editor to delete it than to write an ending himself.

TYPICAL OUTLINES FOR TECHNICAL ARTICLES

Below you'll find a typical outline for each of the twelve kinds of articles we discussed in Chapter 2. Use these outlines as a guide when preparing your own articles. The sample outlines will save you time and energy. And they'll get you easier admission to editorial offices when you submit a query. But a word of caution—use these outlines only as guides. Fill in your own data for the particular story you are considering.

PLANT DESCRIPTIONS

I. Lead
   A. Name, owner, and location of the plant
   B. Type of plant or unit
   C. Outstanding features of the plant design
   D. What's expected from this feature
II. Details of the plant   [Middle]
   A. Location and its effect on plant equipment
      1. Unusual local conditions
      2. Effect of these conditions on plant design
      3. Steps taken to cope with unusual local conditions
   B. Equipment schemes considered
      1. Discussion of usable schemes
      2. Reasons for choosing scheme used
      3. Advantages of scheme used
   C. Principal equipment
      1. Type
      2. Manufacturer
      3. Capacity
      4. Utilities (fuel, electricity, etc.)
      5. Operating characteristics (efficiency, speed, etc.)
      6. Unusual features
      7. Tabulation of principal units and their features
   D. Plant flow details
      1. Flow diagram
      2. Paths of the major and minor materials or fluids

       3. Flow rates, pressures, temperatures
       4. Flow variations with load changes
  E. Operating details
       1. Control systems
       2. Automatic controls
       3. Manual controls
       4. Manpower requirements
       5. Operating cycles
       6. Personnel work schedules
       7. Raw materials supply
       8. Materials storage
       9. Safety features
     10. Security features
     11. Utilities
     12. Other details
  F. Personnel facilities
       1. Locker rooms
       2. Wash and shower areas
       3. Feeding
       4. Recreation
       5. Medical
       6. Educational
       7. Parking
       8. Others
  G. Design advantages
       1. Initial-cost savings
       2. Operating-cost savings
       3. Manpower savings
       4. Other savings
  H. Expected results
       1. Product output
       2. Efficiency
       3. Operating life
       4. Over-all advantages
       5. Other expectations
III. What this plant means to the industry   [End]
  A. Today
  B. Tomorrow (several years distant)
  C. Design or construction trends to watch

PROCESS DESCRIPTIONS

I. Lead
   A. Name, licensor, and application of the process
   B. Name, owner, and location of the plant
   C. Outstanding features of the process
II. Process detail   [Middle]
   A. Product
      1. Rated output
      2. Properties (purity, specific gravity, density, etc.)
      3. Other characteristics
   B. Raw materials
      1. Name
      2. Quality
      3. Consumption
      4. Catalysts
      5. Chemicals
      6. Other raw materials
   C. Flow details
      1. Flow diagram
      2. Paths of major and minor materials or fluids
      3. Flow rates, pressures, temperatures
      4. Flow variations with output changes
      5. Catalyst consumption and regeneration
      6. Chemical reactions
   D. Process equipment
      1. Type
      2. Manufacturer
      3. Capacity
      4. Operating characteristics
      5. Utilities
      6. Unusual features
      7. Tabulation of principal units and their features
   E. Operating details
      1. Control systems
      2. Automatic controls
      3. Manual controls
      4. Manpower requirements
      5. Operating cycles
      6. Personnel work schedules
      7. Raw-materials supply

        8. Materials storage
        9. Safety features
      10. Security features
      11. Utilities
      12. Other details
    F. Personnel facilities
       1. Locker room
       2. Wash and shower areas
       3. Feeding
       4. Recreation
       5. Medical
       6. Educational
       7. Parking
       8. Others
    G. Process advantages
       1. Initial-cost savings
       2. Operating-cost savings
       3. Manpower savings
       4. Other savings
    H. Expected yields
       1. Product output
       2. Raw-material or charge input
       3. Operating life
       4. Over-all advantages
       5. Other expectations
III. Effect of this process on the industry   [End]
    A. Other installations (location, owner, product, etc.)
    B. Future installations
    C. Design or construction trends of the future

DESIGN PROCEDURES

  I. Lead
    A. Name, size, and type of item to be designed
    B. Principal design problems
    C. How this procedure overcomes these problems
  II. Procedure details   [Middle]
    A. Design requirements
       1. Output, capacity, allowable load, rating, etc.
       2. Allowable atmospheric conditions—temperature, humidity, etc.
       3. Allowable operating conditions

       4. Size and weight
       5. Materials
       6. Appearance, color, finish, packaging
  B. Alternatives meeting the design requirements
       1. Description of each alternative
       2. Advantages of each
       3. Disadvantages of each
       4. Reasons for choosing the alternative chosen
  C. Design problem
       1. Concisely state the whole problem to be solved
       2. Describe the methods for solving it
       3. Reasons for choosing the solution used
  D. Steps to follow
       1. In setting up the problem
       2. In mathematical, graphical, estimating, or other procedures presented
       3. In using tabular, graphical, or other data presented in article
       4. When solution is obtained
  E. Checking results
       1. Reasons for checks
       2. Precautions in making and evaluating checks
       3. Checking intermediate results
       4. Checking final results
       5. Comparing results with those from other methods
  F. Applying the results
       1. To a single unit
       2. To a series of units
       3. To work in your plant
       4. To work done in other plants
       5. To other situations
  G. Other considerations
       1. Materials
       2. Finish
       3. Color
       4. Packaging
       5. Shipping
       6. Price, as related to design
III. Future designs   [End]
  A. Relation of this procedure to future ones
  B. Probable trends in design methods
  C. Other considerations

PRODUCT FUNCTIONS

I. Lead
  A. Name, type, and size of product
  B. Typical applications of the product
  C. Problems met in product use
  D. Problems solved by use of the product
II. How the product works   [Middle]
  A. Product description
    1. Moving parts
    2. Stationary parts
    3. Other parts
    4. Materials used for parts
    5. Similar types of products
    6. How they compare with others
    7. Needed accessory equipment
  B. Product working cycle
    1. Steps in a cycle, from beginning to end
    2. Pressures, temperatures, flow rates, etc.
    3. Flow pattern in or through the unit
    4. Allowable working ranges of the product
  C. Product operation
    1. Starting procedures
    2. Routine operating procedures
    3. Stopping procedures
    4. Operating pointers
  D. Product maintenance
    1. Routine maintenance
    2. Special overhaul and repair procedures
    3. Tool and other equipment for maintenance
  E. Product selection
    1. Determining size or capacity required
    2. Choosing the most suitable unit
    3. Checking the choice
  F. Product application
    1. Installation
    2. Initial start-up
    3. Operating the new unit with existing ones
    4. Other considerations
III. Results this product gives   [End]
  A. Output, efficiency, savings, etc.
  B. Summary of major advantages

CALCULATION METHODS

I. Lead
   A. Item to be computed
   B. Difficulties met in the computation
   C. How this method reduces these difficulties

II. Calculation procedure   [Middle]
   A. Data needed
      1. Variables, constants, and other factors
      2. Where to obtain these data
      3. Precautions in assembling data
      4. Other considerations
   B. Equations or computational methods used
      1. Basis of equations or methods
      2. How equations or methods were developed
      3. Symbols used, and their units
   C. Illustrative example
      1. State problem
      2. Solve this problem in a series of steps
      3. Explain each step and the reason for it
      4. Note the major exceptions likely to occur
      5. Other considerations
      6. Present one or more additional illustrative problems, if they are needed to explain the method

III. Limitations of the method   [End]
   A. Where the method is suitable for use
   B. Where it is unsuitable for use
   C. Special precautions

GRAPHICAL SOLUTIONS

I. Lead
   A. Problem to be solved
   B. Advantages of a graphical solution

II. Solution details   [Middle]
   A. Description of the graphs or charts
      1. Equations or data on which charts are based
      2. Symbols, and their units
      3. Limits and other ranges used in the charts
      4. Calculations for which the charts are suitable
      5. Where the charts cannot be used

B. Illustrative example
    1. State problem
    2. Solve this problem, using the charts
    3. Explain each step in the solution
    4. Note the major exceptions that may occur
    5. Other considerations
    6. Present one or more additional illustrative problems and solutions, if they are needed to explain the charts

III. Advantages of this method   [End]
  A. Time
  B. Labor
  C. Expense

OPERATING PROCEDURES

I. Lead
  A. Why careful operating procedures are needed
  B. Advantages of using correct procedures

II. Recommended operating methods   [Middle]
  A. Steps in start-ups
    1. Before the machine is running
    2. Items to check
    3. Putting the machine in motion
    4. Checks during and immediately after starting
    5. Other precautions
  B. Routine operation
    1. Items to check at regular intervals
    2. Recording the items checked
    3. Routine lubrication, fueling, servicing, etc.
    4. Other routine operating needs
  C. Stopping procedures
    1. Reducing load, speed, capacity, etc.
    2. Cutting off power
    3. Stopping motion
    4. Checks to make when motion stops
    5. Other procedures

III. How to obtain best operating results   [End]
  A. Correct procedures
  B. Records
  C. Personnel training
  D. Regular maintenance

MAINTENANCE PROCEDURES

I. Lead
   A. Name, type, size, and service conditions of unit
   B. Problems usually met in maintenance
   C. How correct procedures overcome maintenance problems
II. Step-by-step procedures   [Middle]
   A. Detecting trouble
      1. From operating records
      2. From performance tests
      3. How to make performance tests
      4. Trouble warnings—noise, smells, vibration, output reduction, etc.
      5. Other ways to detect trouble
   B. Disassembly methods
      1. Unit shutdown
      2. Removal of working fluid (drainage, etc.)
      3. Opening, removing, and inspecting casing, shell, or cover
      4. Precautions during disassembly (tagging of parts, use of special tools, etc.)
      5. Safety considerations
      6. Other considerations
   C. Overhaul and repair methods
      1. Removal of working parts
      2. Inspection of working parts
      3. Repair of worn parts
      4. When to replace old parts with new ones
      5. Other overhaul and repair methods
   D. Reassembly
      1. Precautions before starting reassembly
      2. Steps in reassembly
      3. Testing the reassembled unit
      4. Other considerations in reassembly
III. Getting more from maintenance   [End]
   A. Records
   B. Personnel training
   C. Correct operating methods

QUESTION AND ANSWER
  I. Lead
    A. Basic question whose answer defines the field to be covered by the article.
    B. One or more additional questions amplifying the first one
 II. Specific coverage   [Middle]
    A. Questions and answers selected to cover the particular areas chosen for the article
    B. Additional related questions that add to the reader's knowledge about the article subject matter
III. Other coverage   [End]
    A. Questions devoted to future expectations
    B. Examination questions, or other specialized questions the reader should be familiar with

MANAGEMENT TECHNIQUES
  I. Lead
    A. Reasons why the article material is needed
    B. Who needs and can use the material
    C. What problems it will solve for the reader
 II. The problem and its solution   [Middle]
    A. State the problem
      1. Where it occurs
      2. Usual difficulties it presents
      3. Other characteristics of the problem
    B. Usual solutions
      1. Common methods
      2. Other methods
      3. Why they fail, or are only partially effective
      4. Why better solutions are needed
    C. The new or better solution
      1. How it is superior to older solutions
      2. What its advantages are
      3. Other reasons for its use
    D. Applying the new solution
      1. Under usual conditions
      2. Under unusual conditions
      3. Precautions in using the method
      4. Other considerations in using the method

III. Getting the most from the new solution   [End]
   A. Personnel factors
   B. Financial factors
   C. Other factors

DEPARTMENTAL FEATURES

I. Lead
   A. Short, concise statement of the problem
   B. Agreement or disagreement with existing methods, opinions, or other data
II. Main thought of the feature   [Middle]
   A. How, why, where, or when the method, idea, data, etc., can be used, changed, corrected, etc.
   B. Main reasons for recommending or criticizing the method, idea, or data
III. Action urged   [End]
   A. To secure better results
   B. To give continued success

NEWS ITEMS

I. Lead
   A. What, who, when, where, why, how
II. Detail of the story   [Middle]
   A. Technical data
   B. Business data
   C. Personnel details
   D. Consultants, engineers, architects, designers, and others connected with the story
III. Future expectations   [End]

NEW EQUIPMENT ITEMS

I. Lead
   A. Name, type, capacity, and other general details of the unit
   B. Principal advantages
II. Construction data   [Middle]
   A. Materials, model number, color, dimensions, and other details of the unit
   B. Performance characteristics
III. Where to obtain additional information (name and address, including a key letter or number, if one is desired)   [End]

HOW TO USE THESE OUTLINES

There are three steps in the effective use of the outlines in this chapter: (1) Choose the outline that most closely fits your planned article. (2) Prepare a rough listing for your beginning, middle, and end, as in Chapter 3. (3) Insert items from your listing in the appropriate places in the outline.

After choosing the correct outline you will run into one of three situations: the outline may suit your article exactly, it may contain too many items, or it may contain too few. The first situation will rarely occur. If the outline has too many items for your article, simply insert all you have available. Then delete the extra ones from the outline. The extra ones are not an indispensable part of the outline—they are suggestions for the elements of a typical article of one kind.

Where the outline does not contain enough items to provide space for all those in your listing, do the following. Insert all the items from the list that you can. Then, carefully, take the remaining items and insert them where they belong in the over-all scheme of the article. No matter what scheme you use, you should wind up with a good outline, if you give it some thought. Remember—an outline can save you time and energy and spare you grief. So always use one.

SUMMARY

Outlining your articles before you write saves time, energy, and labor. And the finished article has more chance of being accepted because it will have better continuity, will include important points, and will be tailored to the magazine. To outline an article correctly you must assemble your facts and illustrations and analyze them. Then you'll be sure of having a beginning, middle, and end for your article.

CHAPTER CHECK-UP

1. Give seven reasons for outlining an article.
2. What advantages do you gain by outlining?
3. Give the three basic steps in outlining a typical technical article.
4. What major divisions should every article have?
5. Outline three types of technical articles of your choice.
6. How should the outlines in this chapter be used? Give two examples of their use.

Chapter 5

YOU CAN WORK WITH EDITORS

Half the fun of technical writing is working with editors. As a group, business-paper editors are alert, intelligent, informed. You are certain to acquire useful ideas from every editor you meet. But editors are busy. Unless you learn how to work effectively with them you waste time and miss valuable information. Let's see how you can improve your dealings with all business-paper editors.

PICK THE RIGHT MAGAZINE

One of the major complaints of editors today is that they receive too much unsuitable material. Articles are submitted helter-skelter. Editors lose valuable time reading and rejecting this poor material. So your first rule for making and keeping editorial friends is: *Pick the right magazine before submitting any material.* How? Here are three useful hints.

1. *Study the magazines—learn what they are publishing.* Get the last six issues of the business papers you think might run your article. Study each issue, while your article is still in outline form. If you have the time and are interested, set up an analysis chart like Fig. 5-1. Enter the various items in the proper columns as you study an issue. List the number of articles in the issue, the number of pages, words, and illustrations used per article, the types of illustrations, the writing style, the kinds of headlines, the types of articles used, the readers they're intended for, and the kinds of subheads used.

When you've done this for six issues of a magazine, compare the outline of your article (see Chapter 4) with the tabulation. If your

MAGAZINE ANALYSIS FORM					
NAME OF MAGAZINE	USUAL LENGTH OF ARTICLES (Words) (Pages)	NO. OF ILLUS. USED TYPE OF ILLUS. USED	TYPES OF ARTICLES USED	PUBLICATION FREQUENCY	AUTHOR OCCUPATION
Product Engineering	800 – 1000 1000 – 1500 1500 – 2000 2000 – 2500 1,2,3 and 4 pages	2 – 3 3 – 4 4 – 6 6 – 8 *Line drawings; photos; charts*	*Design procedures; Product functions; Calculation methods; Graphical solutions; Management*	*Weekly*	*Engineers, designers; stress analysts; college professors*
Power	200 – 800 800 – 1000 1000 – 1500 1500 – 2000 2000 – 2500 ½,1,2,3 and 4 or more pages	1 – 2 2 – 3 3 – 4 4 – 6 6 – 8 *Photos; charts; line drawings*	*Plant stories; Design procedures; Operating procedures; Maintenance procedures*	*Monthly*	*Plant and power engineers; designers; college professors*

Fig. 5-1. Form for analyzing articles in business magazines.

article is a type used by the magazine and your illustrations are the kind that appear in the issues, you're on the right track. The other items—style, length, and headline—can be tailored to suit the particular magazine. This is why you should pick the magazine while your article is still in outline form. You can alter the handling of your story more readily while it is in outline form than when all the copy is written and illustrations chosen.

2. *Check for other magazines in the field.* If you know of only a few magazines in a field, don't assume there aren't any others. Check. Where? One excellent source of information about business papers is "Business Publication Advertising Rates and Data," published by Standard Rate and Data Service, Inc. Others are "Comprehensive Magazine Directory," published by Commercial Engraving Publishing Company, and "The House Magazine Directory," published by The Gebbie Press.

Once you've learned the names of all the magazines in the field covered by your article, get copies of them. Study and analyze the articles according to the plan in item 1 above.

3. *Study the magazines' ads.* Editors of modern business papers
have nothing to do with the advertising in their magazines. But the
editorial material they choose attracts certain kinds of advertisers. So
in studying the ads you learn the extent of the field covered by the
magazine.

If your article covers a type of product or service advertised in the
magazine, there's an excellent chance of reader interest in your story.
And it's also likely that the editor will be interested.

What if no ads cover your product or service? Don't be discouraged.
There's almost as good a chance of your story being used. For if your
article covers part of the field served by a magazine, there will be
readers for it.

Once you're reasonably certain the editor can use your article, you
can contact him. But be certain your article is right for the magazine.
If there's any doubt in your mind, wait a few weeks and think it over.
Or get six more issues of the magazine and study them. You're almost
certain to find definite preferences, as shown by the articles the
magazine publishes.

Now you may ask two questions: Why spend so much time studying the magazine before contacting the editor? Isn't there an easier
way of learning the editor's requirements than studying six issues?

The answer to the first question is that every minute you spend
studying the magazine before contacting the editor is worthwhile because you learn a great deal about the editor and his publication. Few
technical writers bother to study the magazines before writing. So
you have the jump on them. Your copy will more nearly meet the
editor's needs, and you won't waste his time with unsuitable material.

As for the second question, there are easier ways to learn an editor's needs—but there is no better way than by studying the magazine.
Market data, published for professional writers, give a short summary
of editors' needs. But such data are almost useless when compared to
study of the actual magazine.

In the actual magazine you see what the editor publishes. You
observe the length of story, the types of illustration, the writing style
he prefers and the readers he aims at. Study of the masthead gives
you the names of all the editors on the magazine, and in some cases,
their specialties. You never waste time when studying the magazine
you'd like to write for.

HOW TO CONTACT AN EDITOR

There are five ways of contacting an editor: (1) Call him on the phone. (2) Write him. (3) Have your public relations man call or write him. (4) Ask your firm's advertising agency to call or write him. (5) Speak to the magazine's advertising space salesman, asking him to give your material to the editor. Of these five only the first three should normally be used. If at all possible, steer clear of dealing through an advertising agency or space salesman. Let's take a closer look at each way.

Call the editor. Check with the magazine's masthead. See if an editor is listed for the specialty covering your article. If he is, call and ask for him. When the specialties of the editors are not listed, call the editorial department and ask for the editor handling the subject matter of your article.

Avoid asking for the chief editor, unless the magazine's editorial staff is extremely small (three people or less). The chief editor will only turn you over to an associate or assistant editor handling your subject. By going directly to an associate or assistant editor you save time and have a better chance of having your article accepted. The reason for this is that the associate editor is usually closer to the field and is more actively concerned with actually securing manuscripts than the chief editor. Many chief editors today are more concerned with policy decisions and other administrative duties than they are with manuscript solicitation.

When you have the right editor on the phone, tell him concisely and quickly: (A) who you are, (B) your company affiliation and job title, (C) the subject of your article, and (D) why his readers would be interested in your article.

Concentrate your effort on the reader-interest your article has. Tell the editor exactly why his readers will be interested. Point out the new features you cover, or the old problems you solve. Remember—every good editor has his readers in mind at all times. If you have a story that appeals to his readers, the editor will spot it instantly.

Don't try to sell your story forcibly. You will only build resentment if you try to pressure an editor. Let your story sell itself. To do this, review the story carefully before contacting the editor. Pick out the points of major interest. Tell the editor what they are! If he is interested, he'll tell you what steps to take in submitting your article. Follow these exactly.

Write the editor. Check the masthead as in preparing to call. If you find an editor handling your specialty, write him. If you do not, then write the chief editor.

Make your letter short, concise. As in the telephone approach, give the editor the essential facts he needs to judge your idea. Here's an example of a good query letter:

In the last 30 months, sixteen plants in Illinois converted to high-temperature hot-water heating. Why? Because they're saving anywhere from 10 to 45% on their fuel bills. How? By smart engineering of the installation, intelligent operation, and careful maintenance.

Complete statistics for these plants are available. These statistics include installation, operating, and maintenance costs. Photos and drawings of the installations are also available. The data and illustrations tell a forceful and informative story that will make every engineer in the heating field stop to examine his thinking. Would you be interested in this story? If so, what length would you prefer? How many and what kinds of illustrations would be best?

I am a design engineer with The ABC Engineering Company and have published a number of articles and papers in various technical journals.

Have your public relations man contact the editor. This can save you time and energy. But be certain to supply the PR man with complete, accurate information. If the PR man does not have an extensive technical background, present the facts about your story as simply as possible. Avoid big words, long explanations, and complicated equations. Instead, summarize your story as in item 1 or 2 above. A smart editor will spot a good story within moments after a PR man begins to talk.

Have your firm's ad agency contact the editor. Use this method only when you can't use one of the first three. Give the agency a concise summary of your story. Direct them to have the editor contact you if he wants more information.

This scheme can work well if the agency man contacting the editor forgets advertising completely for the time being. Editors will never buy a story just because there is an ad tie-in. Many editors will be extremely wary of material from an ad agency. But editors also recognize that having the agency make the initial contact can help you. So most editors will listen sympathetically, *if* all mention of advertising is kept out of the conversation.

Speak to the magazine's space salesman. If a space salesman calls on you or someone in your firm, get to know him. While space salesmen have nothing to do with editorial matters, they know the editors personally. Most space salesmen can tell you the specialties of their editors. You can use this information when calling or writing an editor.

Tell the space salesman about your article. If it sounds interesting to him, he may send it to an editor on his magazine. This doesn't mean your article has been accepted—the editor is the only man with authority to accept an article. But it does mean that your article will go directly to the editor concerned, probably with a short note from the salesman.

WHAT TO SHOW AN EDITOR

Suppose, after a call or a query letter, an editor asks for some sample material for your article. What should you show him? There's no simple answer to this. But most editors will be satisfied with (A) your story outline, (B) a few of your illustrations, (C) some of your tables or charts, and (D) any other related material.

Don't try to overpower the editor with a suitcaseful of material. Choose a few of the best items you have. All the editor is trying to get is a quick idea of how you work and the quality of your material. If your presentation shows forethought and consideration your story will almost always sell. But always, always keep in mind that *editors are busy* and *they think of their readers first, themselves second.*

GETTING ALONG WITH EDITORS

Here are seven valuable rules for dealing with business-paper editors. Keep these rules in mind and you'll seldom go wrong.

1. *Think only of the editor's readers.* Don't ever forget that an editor thinks first, last, and always about his readers. Any editor who didn't wouldn't be much of an editor. Check every article idea for reader interest. And make sure to tell the editor why his readers will be interested.

2. Give an editor an exclusive for every feature article. When you decide which magazine is best for your story, go all out to sell the editor on its worth. But don't try to place the story in more than one magazine at a time. If you do you'll antagonize an editor or two. And the next time you come around with a story you may find that the welcome mat has been mislaid.

So give the editor an exclusive on your story; that is, don't submit your story anywhere else until the editor gives you a definite turndown. If the editor accepts your article, don't ever submit it elsewhere, *before or after he publishes it.* Give the editor sole use of your story, unless he tells you he doesn't want the sole right to use it. When giving an editor the exclusive use of your story you assure him of scooping the competition. And every active editor loves to do this, particularly with an outstanding article.

3. Supply good photos. Hire a professional industrial photographer to take your photos. The results are worth every penny you pay him. And when sending the photos to the editor pack them so they can't be bent or folded. Never write on the photos; you may, however, mark on an identifying number with grease pencil. Type the caption on a sheet of paper and attach it to the back of the photo with rubber cement, or make a separate list of captions.

4. Make clean, neat drawings. Put each drawing on a separate sheet. Have all the lettering legible; don't crowd the drawing with it. Number each drawing, and either type or glue its caption on.

5. Type your text neatly. Don't think—just type *everything* in your article double-spaced. This includes text, captions, footnotes, tables, quoted material, bibliography, equations, and mathematical material. Use plain white bond paper. Never use fancy colored paper for articles; editors like white. If you can't type well, pay a typist to prepare a neat, clean typescript of your article. Keep one carbon copy for yourself. If the editor wants two copies of your article, send him the original and one carbon copy.

6. Take the editor's advice—he knows. If an editor is kind enough to tell you how to revise or rewrite your article, listen to him. And do as he says. You'll probably improve your article and writing ability by doing as he says. Remember—article writing is not a long-hair, artistic profession. Instead, it is a workmanlike occupation in which you give a reader useful, important facts in an interesting and easily understood way. So listen to the editor—he knows how to put ideas across.

7. *Be friendly.* Treat editors in a man-to-man way. Every editor is interested in getting the best articles possible for his readers. If you can supply good articles, editors will keep you busy day and night.

Use good taste in dealing with editors. You can treat an editor to lunch, if his firm allows it. But never offer an editor a gift of any kind. He'll probably refuse it, embarrassing both you and himself. The only gift any editor wants from a writer is a good story. And many editors show their appreciation for a good article by paying you an honorarium for it.

HOW TO IRRITATE EDITORS

You can learn as much from what *irritates* editors as you did from how to get along with them. So here are seven ways to irritate an editor. Be certain that you are never guilty of any of these!

1. *Threaten to cut ad space if your article is rejected.* Editors have *nothing* to do with the advertising in their magazines. Many writers don't understand this, so if their article is slighted in some way they scream that their company will cancel its ads in the magazine.

Don't ever try this hoax. It won't work. Why? The editor will probably tell you to go right ahead and cancel every ad for the next hundred years. This still won't change his opinion of your article. An article either stands on its own merits, or it doesn't. Buying every ad page in a business paper will not change the usefulness of an article for the readers.

Threats to cancel ads can lose you many friends. Never threaten, either directly or indirectly. You'll regret it if you do.

2. *Crumple your photos, drawings, or copy.* Mangled illustrations or copy ruin many an editor's faith in people. If you spend a week or more writing an article, take a few minutes to wrap and mail it properly.

Protect all photos with corrugated board. One strong piece is enough. Or use double-thick cardboard. Your postage bill will be a few pennies higher, but your photos, drawings, and copy will arrive safely. And to be sure your material is returned if it's unusable, enclose a stamped, self-addressed envelope.

3. *Pester the editor for a publication date.* When an editor ac-

cepts a good story from you, he plans to run it as soon as he has space for it. So calling him on the phone every few days or writing nasty letters won't help much.

Every business-paper editor has problems. Issue schedules, in which the content of the magazine is planned, are a major problem. Some articles may be too long. Others are too short. Or there may be three articles on the same subject. The schedule must be juggled to make the best possible issue for the readers.

So if publication of your article is delayed, be patient. You'll make lasting friends by showing a little understanding of the other man's problems. And the next time this editor accepts an article from you, watch how soon it runs. Patience pays off in article writing.

4. *Scream at the rewrite of your golden words.* Some business papers rewrite every contributed article they publish. Reason? To get the story across to the reader faster and easier.

Don't feel hurt, then, if your article is rewritten. The published version is probably better than what you submitted. Even if the editor makes a factual error, be gentle in pointing it out to him. Remember —when agreeing to publish your article every editor reserves the right to rewrite if he thinks the material needs it. If you don't want your material rewritten, submit it to a paper that doesn't rewrite.

5. *Bother the editor for copies of the magazine.* Many new writers bother editors incessantly for copies of the issue in which their article appears. They start three weeks before publication and don't miss a day until the magazine is out. Again, be patient.

If possible, learn who handles tear sheets and reprints in the editorial office. This is often a gal. By being sweet and considerate to her you can arrange to get a copy of the issue as soon as it comes out. And you won't be bothering the editor.

6. *Hound the editor for payment.* Some business papers pay their honorarium on acceptance of contributed material. Others wait until publication. Find out which scheme "your" magazine uses. Then be patient.

Article payments are seldom delayed. But occasionally the accounting department will be overloaded. Your payment may then be delayed a week or two, perhaps longer. Give the check at least two months, after publication, to arrive. If it doesn't come by then, call the magazine. But be nice! Everyone makes a mistake now and then.

7. *Make extensive changes in your reprints.* This, your last way of being mean, can make editors wish they had never learned to read. Don't make any changes in reprints, other than corrections of typographical errors or errors of fact.

Typos can't be helped. The best of printers make them. Editors will never object to correcting these, free of charge. Factual errors that are the editor's fault will also be corrected. But these are usually few.

Errors that you as author are responsible for make editors unhappy. And if you want to make text changes for reasons of company policy, you're certain to run into resistance.

WHAT EDITORS CAN DO TO YOUR ARTICLES

When you submit an article to an editor you should be ready to allow him to alter it to suit his readers. For an editor can: (1) rewrite to suit his needs, (2) delete parts of the text or illustrations and tables, (3) ask detailed questions about the material, (4) publish your material without clearance from you (few do this, but they can, if they wish), (5) ask for an exclusive story, and (6) reject your material.

So be sure your story says what you mean, before you submit it. Then you'll run into fewer problems with rewrites or cut articles. And you'll find that the more you work with editors, the fewer the changes that will be made in your articles. Your writing will be better and your choice of article length more accurate. But be ready to accept the changes the editor recommends.

ARTICLE LENGTH

When you contact an editor he may tell you the number of words he'd like your story to contain. But many editors today do not specify article length in words. Instead, they speak of a one-pager, a two-pager, a three-pager, etc. The reason for using these expressions is that editors continually think in terms of the *published* article. With the large number of illustrations used in modern articles, it is difficult to set a word limit.

From studying back issues and making notes in a tabulation like Fig. 5-1, you'll get a good idea of how many words there are in articles of various published lengths. As a guide, you can also use the tabulation below. But remember—it is only a rough guide. The number of words or illustrations may vary as much as 50 per cent, plus or minus.

Typical Article Length

Number of published pages	Approximate number of words	Number of illustrations
½	300–400	1 or 2
1	800	1 or 2
2	1,500–2,000	1–6
3	2,500	1–6
4	3,000–3,500	1–8
6	5,000	1–12
8	5,500–6,500	1–15

Decide how many words, illustrations, and tables you'll have before you start to write. Count each table as equivalent to an illustration. Count the number of words in the article after you finish writing. If you have twice as many words as you planned, cut until you are closer to the original estimate. But if you are only a few hundred words over, don't bother to cut, particularly in long articles. The editor will do this if it's necessary.

PLAY SAFE

Get permission for all material you use, *before* you submit your article to a magazine. If you want to quote from published material, *write the publisher, not the author*. Remember—a few letters requesting permission for use of quoted material will save you many nights of lost sleep. And the editor will respect your caution. Save all permission letters. You may have to produce them at a later date.

And get permission from your firm to publish the article, *before* you submit it to a magazine. Articles can be a major asset in your advance up the ladder in your company. But if you publish an article without company approval you may run into trouble. So play safe— get permission before sending any article to an editor.

SUMMARY

Good relations with business-paper editors are as important to you as sound article ideas and well-written copy. You'll never publish an article without dealing with an editor—either personally or by mail. So the sooner you learn how to work with editors, the sooner you'll achieve success in your writing. Learn now, while you have time to study and make plans for the future. Your writing experiences will be much pleasanter and more fruitful if you make full use of all the pointers given in this chapter.

CHAPTER CHECK-UP

1. What are three good ways of finding the right magazine for your story?
2. What can you learn by studying past issues of a magazine?
3. Name three publications listing business papers.
4. Name five ways of contacting an editor. Discuss each.
5. What should you tell an editor about your article when speaking or writing to him?
6. Write a query letter for an article on (*a*) auto tires, (*b*) radar-receiver design, and (*c*) diesel-engine manufacture.
7. Give seven rules for getting along with editors. Discuss each rule.
8. List seven habits that are sure to irritate editors. Tell how you can avoid each of these.
9. What rights has an editor once he accepts your article?
10. What kind of clearance should you get for an article before submitting it? Why?

Chapter 6

WRITE A SNAPPY ARTICLE
TITLE AND LEAD

Business-paper editors come in all sizes, shapes, and types. Talk to a hundred editors and you'll find only two traits common to them all. These are: (1) Their readers are kings. (2) They judge an article by reading it from the beginning toward the end. We'll overlook the first trait here because it's discussed elsewhere in this book. We'll spend the rest of this chapter on the second trait.

WORKING TITLES WIN

Since the editor starts reading at the beginning of your article, its title must be good. And the title must be good if it's to stop a hurried reader as he flips through the magazine. Remember, your article is competing for attention with every other article in the issue. So learn now how to write good titles (or heads, as they're also called).

Your article title should (1) convince the reader he *just has to* read your article, and (2) help him move into the text smoothly, with minimum effort. It must "work" for you.

If you stop to analyze good article titles you'll find that they are brief, accurate, and often in the active voice. Don't depend on the subject matter of the title to give the punch needed. Besides *what* the title says, it's important *how* it says it.

Good titles use sentences more often than phrases. They emphasize newness, or "nowness." The good title combines clarity, detail, and vividness. Benefits mentioned in a good title are specific—the reader doesn't have to hunt for the benefits in the text. Many good titles tell a story, or promise one.

And many good titles are the W type—they use *why, when, where, who,* or *what.* Or they imply the use of or the answer to one or more of these words.

HOW TO WRITE WINNING TITLES

Use a label type of head when first thinking of your article. Thus, if you are doing an article on *plywood adhesives,* use these two words to identify the article in your mind. But they would not make a very effective title. Why? Because they are just a label. They don't tell the reader anything more than the subject of the article. There is no incentive for him to read the article, unless plywood adhesives happen to be extremely important to him.

To improve this title, let's try putting it in the active voice. You can do this before you write your article or after it's finished. Some technical writers prefer to wait until they finish the article. Then if there has been any change in the slant of the article the title can be altered to suit.

But if you start with a good title it can help slant your thinking during writing. And if you live with the title while you're writing your article, you may find a number of new ways to improve the title. So take your choice. We'll try to start with a good title.

Now we know that the elements of this title are the two words *plywood adhesives.* Next, as you have seen, you should try to get some newness or "nowness" in the title. Also, the title should be as nearly a sentence as possible.

Let's say the adhesives you'll discuss in the article are stronger, have longer life, and are cheaper than others. That immediately suggests this title:

New Plywood Adhesives Are Stronger, Long-lived, Cheaper

Working on this title you might come up with:

Save with New, Stronger Long-life Plywood Adhesives

Or you could phrase it:

Long-life Plywood Adhesives Offer Extra Strength, Savings

You could find a number of other variations. The important point to see here is that any of these three is better than the label type of title you started with. These three promise the reader something for his time. And if he does no more than read the article title, he learns something.

Once you have worked up three or more titles for your article, make a list of them. Then try these titles on your friends. Keep a record of their votes. Put the titles aside while you write the article. When you come back to the titles, see if your opinion agrees with the votes. If it does, use the winning title; if it doesn't, try to rework the titles. Use the one that appeals most to you.

EXAMPLES OF GOOD TITLES

Here are 16 examples of good article titles. Note how many of them incorporate the principles you learned at the beginning of this chapter.

> New Process Produces Instant Non-fat Dry Milk
> Shop-built Equipment Repairs Tire Damages
> Transistors Convert Sine Waves to Pulses
> Addition of . . .
>   More Transformers and Feeder Capacity
>   . . . Eliminates Overloads at Chicago's Merchandise Mart
> Nine Key Factors Round Out
>   KRAFT SANITATION
> An Old Mill
>   Is Brought up to date
> New Cold Forming Process Saves Time and Material
> Magnetic-tape Pickup Has DC Response
> Want a Free Ambulance Ride?
> Who Says Women Aren't Salesmen?
> IDEAS: Where Do You Find Them?
> Refineries Aren't Top Smog Makers
> Strikers Return—But Everyone Loses
> Once a PA—Now a Sales Manager
> Early Motor Truck Uses—From Beer Delivery to War Service
> Take a Good Look at Yourself—What's Your Attitude On. . . .

You can write good titles for all your articles. But it takes time and practice. From now on, study the title of every article you read. Note how good titles "hook" you, causing you to read the text of the article.

And don't be afraid of using subheads in your article title. A subhead can do much for your article. Thus:

> Sweat-drenched powdermen loading holes find that . . .
> Digging Tecolite Tunnel is Hot Work

Or use a short subhead:

> A case study of . . .
> Complete Electric Radiant Heating

Here's another good one:

> How Esso Standard Uses
> Remote Automatic Tank Gaging

Good titles never come easily—not even to experienced writers and editors. So if you sweat over a title for thirty minutes, don't become discouraged. Others do it all the time!

AFTER THE TITLE COMES THE LEAD

Like the title, your lead paragraph must hold the reader. If it doesn't, he'll flip the pages to the next article. Remember—you're competing for his time and attention. And if you want to be read—and who doesn't?—you must make your lead paragraph worth his time. How? Let's see.

While you can devise an infinite number of leads for your story, you'll find that most business papers use one of nine types for many of their stories. These types are: (1) summary, (2) descriptive, (3) problem-solution, (4) comparison, (5) question, (6) purpose, or objective, (7) interpretive, (8) news, and (9) historical.

No matter which type of lead you choose, give the reader the key facts about your story in the first paragraph. If this makes the first paragraph too long, use two paragraphs to present your facts. Don't, ordinarily, use more than two paragraphs because your reader may lose interest. Here are examples of these various leads.

Summary. To write this type of lead, list all the pertinent facts in your story in the order of their importance. You'll probably have too many for one or two paragraphs. So pick the three or four most pertinent facts and concentrate on these. Here's how the magazine *Steel* used the summary type of lead for one of its articles:

> Open hearth charging time has been whacked 55 per cent at Armco's Middletown, Ohio plant. The reduction from 3½ to 1½ hours was made possible by improved materials handling methods.

Basic modification over present methods is in the use of a hoist for lifting the charging materials from ground level. Automatic operation of the various elements in the material handling sequence is the installation's salient feature.

Note the shortness of the first two sentences. Yet both are loaded with information. The reader can decide from these two if it's worth his while to read further.

Descriptive. Here you can pack the main thought of the article into one sentence. This is often the first sentence in the article. You can use a definition or a statement of fact to arrest your reader's attention. Or you can tersely give details of a trend or a prediction of future events. Here's a lead paragraph from the magazine *Mill and Factory*, showing the use of a descriptive start:

Rototrol rotating regulators can provide automatic operation of the electrical equipment that drives industry's multiplicity of machines in a simple and reliable manner. Such a regulator is similar in design to a standard d-c generator, except that it has several field windings designed and connected in various ways depending on the regulating problem. It can be used to regulate any quantity that can be measured electrically such as voltage, current, power, torque, speed, and position.

Problem solution. This lead is tops where your article is concerned with the solution of a basic problem. You'll find it popular in articles about new plants or the modernization of old ones. Here's a good example from the magazine *The Paper Industry*:

With two years experience to back it up, the Ohio Boxboard Company, Rittman, Ohio, has pinned the credit for better quality paper, easier maintenance of equipment, and reduced accidents on their engineered lighting system.

Note here that although the problem is not stated directly, it is clearly implied by the advantages secured from the solution used.

Comparison. To use this type of lead you must have a story in which there's a choice between two or more methods, devices, or schemes. Often you'll compare the familiar with the unfamiliar. This sets the scene for your reader, helping him move easily into your story. *American Machinist* used the comparison lead like this:

As a coolant, water is superior to any other material. Tap water is therefore the best cutting fluid where high cooling is required. But tap water is so corrosive that it can be used only where rusting of the machine tool and work can be tolerated. Following water in cooling ability, in order of decreasing efficiency, are: water-oil emulsions; low-viscosity oils; and high-viscosity oils.

Question. Use this lead when you can summarize your article in one or two short simple questions. By keeping the questions simple, you make the lead easier for readers to follow. Here's how *Plant Engineering* used the question lead:

Why did the bearing in that motor generator set burn out so soon? Was the lubrication at fault? Maybe so, but in many such cases the cause was born the day the set was put into operation and has its roots in two possibilities: (1) improper installation of the coupling; and/or (2) improper selection of the coupling.

Purpose or objective. Here you tell the reader what your article is about. This type of lead may give you trouble when you try to write it. Why? Well to tell the reader what your story is about, you must have thought it through. And not every writer does this before he starts to write. Here's an example of how a writer thought through his (about motor enclosures) story for *Factory Management and Maintenance:*

This article describes the two general types—open, and totally enclosed motors. It identifies the eight standardized enclosures by photographs and by brief definitions. It tells where each is best used, and lists typical applications.

Note the conciseness of this lead. Yet it, along with the article title, tells you exactly what to expect from the story. What more need a reader know before he decides to read more, or turn the page?

Interpretive. Here you orient the reader's mind to your story. You may be covering a new development in his industry. Or you may be presenting conclusions based on a study, or predicting the future based on existing facts. You can also use this lead to connect a seemingly unrelated subject to a current problem. Here's how *Electric Light and Power* magazine used this type of lead:

The magnetic amplifier is at last being recognized at its true value. Although its basic principles have been known for many years it is only recently that its quick response, lack of moving or delicate parts, high amplification, and accuracy are being utilized. Now with servo mechanisms being used for everything from flying an airplane to toasting a slice of bread, the uses for a static device such as the magnetic amplifier are being considered all along the line. Such an application is in generator excitation control where quick response, reliability, and minimum maintenance requirements are vital.

News. This type resembles the newspaper lead. Use it to tell something the industry in general didn't know before. This type of lead is ideal for significant first installations and major engineering or technical achievements. *Electrical World* made good use of the news lead in this case:

The year-long study Detroit Edison and Dow Chemical companies made on industrial use of atomic energy showed definitely that a nuclear reactor can be used to produce electricity on a commercial basis.

Now the question is, how can a nuclear reactor be developed to deliver energy at a cost competitive with a normal source of heat?

Historical. Be careful when choosing the historical lead. You could use it for almost every story, if you wanted to. But most readers aren't interested in a historical lead because they're after results—not bygone events. So choose the historical lead only when your article tells of the evolution of a device, machine, firm, individual, or idea. Here's an example of this type of lead as used by *Paper Trade Journal* in a story about the uses of paper in the electrical industry:

Paper has played an important role in the manufacture of electrical apparatus since the birth of the electrical industry. In the beginning, electrical manufacturers used cellulosic and asbestos fiber-base papers. Cellulosic paper had suitable physical properties, was a good dielectric medium, was relatively economical, could be secured in abundance and could be treated or otherwise modified in many ways to improve its properties. It was used for applications at moderate temperatures up to 105 degrees C. Although asbestos papers had poorer physical and electrical properties, they were desirable for certain applications where the temperature might rise to 125 degrees C. As time passed, cellulosic and asbestos fiber-base papers having special properties were developed by refinements in paper manufacture: chemical treatment of the cellulosic pulps; removal of magnetic conducting material from the pulp by use of magnets and traps and other means; and treatment of the paper with various varnishes, and sizings.

GOOD LEADS SCORE HIGH

Aim at leads that have interest-getting ideas. Use short, accurate sentences in your lead. You'll catch many a reader, as well as the editor. But, more important, you'll write your article better. Why? Let's see.

Good leads (1) gear your mind to your article, (2) give you a picture of where you're going, (3) speed your writing, and (4) give you more momentum to finish your article.

The accurately written lead gears your attention to the essentials of your story. It tells you exactly how to write your story, because in most articles the body just fills out the lead. Remember—there is no room for wasted words in today's technical article. If you set your thinking in the right direction at the start, your writing goes faster. And it's less painful along the way.

Just as important is the stored energy or momentum that a good lead builds in your mind. With the essence of your article neatly stated in the lead, you can dive into the detailed part of your story with complete enthusiasm. And never overlook the importance of an enthusiastic belief in your article. It gives an urgency to your writing that readers recognize and like. Your story moves swiftly and accurately from the lead to its logical end.

Outstanding technical writing requires a high degree of skill. The sooner you recognize this and try to make each story better than the last, the faster you will be recognized and published. So make your message urgent and timely—you'll win and hold the attention of more readers and editors.

SUMMARY

Working titles for your articles win readers. This has been proved in every kind of of modern publication. Good titles often emphasize newness, or "nowness." Start with a label title and work it into an active, interest-catching one. Once you have a good title for your article, write the lead. Choose from one of the nine types given in this chapter. Or combine two or more to develop an urgent, timely opening for your article. The right lead helps you overcome inertia, gives your writing a vibrancy that makes readers look for your by-line every time they open a magazine in your field.

CHAPTER CHECK-UP

1. Name two traits most editors have. Why are these traits important to you as a writer?
2. What are the advantages of a good title for your article?
3. What are the characteristics of good article titles? Select five article titles having one or more of these characteristics.
4. Describe the steps you would use to write an article title. Choose three subjects and write a good article title for each. Explain the steps you followed in each case.
5. What are the nine kinds of leads you can use for technical articles? Describe each type.
6. Choose six technical magazines or business papers and analyze the kinds of leads used in each. What leads predominate? Why do you think these were used?
7. Write nine leads for articles on subjects of your choice. Write each lead so that it illustrates one of the nine types discussed in this chapter.
8. Give three examples of how you could combine two types of leads for a more effective opening for an article.

Chapter 7

KEEP THE MIDDLE LEAN

A snappy lead gets your reader into your article. But you will not keep him there unless the rest of your story is interesting. To hold today's reader you must present your story quickly and concisely. So you must keep your article lean in the middle. In this chapter you will learn many ways to keep your story moving. These methods will also make your writing better and clearer. Let's see what these methods are and how you can apply them to every article you write.

KEEP IT LEAN

There are five rules for making the body of your article interesting. These are: (1) Be concise. (2) Stick to your outline. (3) Keep your story in mind. (4) Write a little each day. (5) Finish soon.

Be concise. The modern technical reader wants his facts in a hurry. He is usually a busy man and can't waste time on an article that wanders. So move directly from your lead into the most important part of your story. To do this, use good transitional devices. These are described later in this chapter.

Stick to your outline. If you start to make major changes in your outline after you've written your lead, you may later have to rewrite the lead. If you have used one of the outlines in Chapter 4 you can be reasonably sure that it will need only minor changes. Follow your outline. It will help your writing, and your story will flow more smoothly.

Keep your story in mind. Some writers refer to this as being "in focus." As long as you keep your story in mind there is no danger of wandering from your subject. It is wandering that causes a story to

slow down and bore the reader. You may find it helpful to write a
short summary of the main points of your story. Keep this in front of
you while you write. Read it frequently, particularly before you begin
writing each day. With a little mental discipline you should be able
to stay in focus at all times while you are writing your article.

Write a little each day. Never try to write an article unless you have
enough time to finish the writing within about four weeks. Then you
will be certain to keep to your story and follow your outline. If you
allow several days to pass between writing sessions you will find that
it takes longer to get started again. This wastes your time and energy.
By writing a little each day, even only a page, you keep your article
in your mind and you can write it better. Also, by writing each day
you build good mental habits of concentration and willingness to
work. After some experience you will learn that no matter what you
are writing, the best way to finish is to work on the project each day.
Your thoughts will flow better and the finished job will have more
unity.

Finish soon. Don't drag out your writing job. By finishing quickly
you give your writing a certain urgency that the reader will recognize.
He will realize that you are trying to tell the complete story in as few
words as possible. He will follow your article with interest because
he knows that he will obtain enough information to repay him for
the time he spends in reading it.

USE BODY BUILDERS

The lead of your article must *catch* the reader's interest. The body
of your article must *build* from the lead and give the reader all the
facts the lead promises. To do this the body of your article must be
strong and full of useful facts. If it isn't, the reader will feel he wasted
the time he spent in reading your article. The next time he sees your
by-line he may skip the article. So never short-change your readers.
They will resent it more than you think. Some readers may even write
the editor. This can seriously damage your future relations with that
editor.

If you write the body of your article well, your readers will read it
faster, remember it longer, understand the subject better, and enjoy
the article more. Let's see how you can make the body of your article
better.

To write the best article possible on a given subject you should (1) know your audience and purpose, (2) develop your subject from the lead, (3) cite cases and give examples, (4) use illustrations to tell part of your story, (5) compare the new with the old, and (6) cite advantages. You may not be able to use all of these in one article. But if you use three or more you can be certain that your readers will benefit. Let's take a closer look at each of these items.

1. *Know your audience and purpose.* Before you start to write the body of your article your first thought should be: Who will read what I write? Remember at all times that you are writing for real people—engineers, scientists, technicians, students, or other people in your field. Decide exactly for whom you are writing. If most of your readers will be college graduates, the wording you choose will be different from that for technicians who did not go beyond high school. But just because your reader has a college degree does not mean you can choose words that are a yard long. No matter who your readers are, you will get your message across faster and easier if you choose short, familiar words. If you work at it your writing can be both simple enough to be read with ease and understanding by a poor reader and interesting enough to hold the attention of a good reader.

Knowing your reader and keeping him in mind at all times is one of the most important rules for successful article writing. So try to form a mental image of your typical reader. Keep him in mind while you write. Use the words he does; choose illustrations that use the same symbols he uses; tell your story in his terms. Then you will be assured of a wide readership and appreciation.

Write with a purpose. What are you trying to do in the body of your article? If the answer to this question is not clear in your mind, you can be certain the reader will not understand your article or its purpose.

So write your purpose on a slip of paper, in as few words as possible. Keep this paper in front of you while you write. Make every paragraph of the body of your article a step to helping the reader understand the purpose of your writing.

2. *Develop your subject from the lead.* Bridge the gap from the lead of your article to the body with a good transition. The simplest transition is a word; typical useful transitional words are *and, but, so, instead, then, for, thus,* etc.

Other transitional devices include a contrast, an exception, a contradiction, a review of the previous text, steps in a procedure, and a series of related ideas. Let's take a look at a few typical transitional devices used to develop the subject of an article from its lead. Each example given below contains the first few paragraphs of an article. Study these examples to learn how other writers provide a smooth passage of ideas from the lead to the body of the article. Note that almost all the examples in this chapter are pertinent excerpts, not complete articles.

Most outstanding among the aspects of today's food business is its definite trend away from the small scale and toward the large scale. The economic historians direct our attention to the shattering of older 19th Century institutional patterns by the Industrial Revolution, as it carried us through the great mergers of 1890–1904 and 1918–1928.

Now, mergers are again occurring rapidly, and this "Automation Revolution" is being hailed—or condemned—as a force comparable with the Industrial Revolution itself.[1]

"America's first all-air-conditioned university" is the title claimed by the University of Dallas at Dallas, Texas.

Because Dallas swelters through long stretches of 100F weather, university trustees decided that air conditioning would aid the academic atmosphere. Accordingly, when they started to erect all new buildings last year, air conditioners were included in the initial plans.

The university's president, F. Kenneth Brasted, says the trustees were convinced that the health and comfort of students and faculty alike would benefit greatly from this move. The long periods of hot weather, particularly during the summer session, were a handicap to study in the classrooms and in the residence halls. Watching more and more commercial buildings and homes around Dallas convert to air conditioning for relief, the trustees felt that it was sure to be installed eventually. So they reasoned, why not now?—and included it in the buildings as they were erected.[2]

In tooling for mass production of the Nike missile, Douglas was moving into uncharted territory. All the original manufacturing operations on

[1] From C. E. French and W. A. Jarrett, Grow Larger to Survive, *Food Engineering*, March, 1958.

[2] From Anonymous, It's 30° Cooler Inside at Dallas U, *Electrical World*, Oct. 7, 1957.

the missile components were first put into production and proven out in Douglas plants.

In the crash production program that developed, however, it was necessary to make use of numerous vendors. At present, four major sub-contractors and more than 200 vendors contribute to Nike-Ajax production.

Production of parts to the exacting standards required for missiles and in quantities much greater than normally encountered in aircraft work required the development of many special machines and techniques.[3]

Wet compressed air is an expensive nuisance. It can rust air tools and cause excessive wear by washing off lubricating film from wearing surfaces. It carries dirt and sediment through pipes and collects in low spots causing water hammer, which jars loose scale, rust and dirt. When exposed to freezing temperatures it can plug or even burst piping.

How water gets into compressed air lines and how it can be kept out are questions that are important to mine operators because of the wide use of air as power. It is becoming increasingly important with the growing applications of air to tools, machines and controls of all types.[4]

3. Cite cases and use examples. Empty words are the surest way to bore your reader. You can write ten pages telling him how a machine saves money. But these ten pages will not be anywhere nearly as convincing as one paragraph describing an actual installation of the machine and stating the number of dollars it saves in a given time. So play safe; show your reader by actual cases what you are trying to prove to him. And don't be satisfied with only one case. If you have the facts available for two or three, cite each case. For the more cases you can cite, the better your chances of convincing your reader. But do not cite more than about five similar cases. If you do you may lose the reader by boredom.

When choosing your cases try to have them as different as possible. Then your reader will see that the principles you are discussing are usable in a number of different circumstances. Study the techniques used in the following typical cases cited in articles:

Plant mergers have in recent years been most pronounced among manufacturers of food and kindred products. Number of firms in this group

[3] From A. Ashburn and G. H. De Groat, The Nike-Ajax: Building the First Mass-production Missile, *American Machinist*, Dec. 16, 1957.

[4] From A. N. Gustafson, Use These Suggestions for Dry Compressed Air, *Engineering and Mining Journal*, Dec., 1957.

declined nearly 40% in the 5 years between 1946 and 1951. And number of firm discontinuances during recent years has been much larger than number of firm starts.

As late as 1939, our food establishments averaged less than 20 workers per establishment. But by 1954 they averaged 40.9 (Table 1). Increased efficiency has allowed each establishment to up output even more than employee numbers.

For example, recent research at Purdue shows the dairy manufactured-products field achieving a given output with about one-third as many inputs as were required in 1919. Other food spheres, including fluid milk, have shown somewhat similar advances. To gain such efficiencies, size must often be increased.[5]

These changes in temperature and pressure are responsible for condensation in any compressed air system wherever it may be.

It can happen even in very dry climates. For example, if free air at 50% relative humidity—rather dry for atmospheric air—were compressed to 100 psi and cooled to room temperature, it would then have relative humidity of 400%. This is foggy and any further compression or cooling would precipitate water.

Moisture is more of a problem in humid climate. For a typical case, suppose that it is a hot, humid day—temperature 90 deg. F and humidity is 80%. A compressor is delivering 200 cfm at 80 lb gage pressure. Each cubic foot of atmospheric air at these conditions contains 0.00175 lb of water. Since 200 cfm are drawn into compressor, total intake is 0.35 lb per minute. This wet air is then compressed to 80 psi.

Compression heats the air so much that it will carry all the moisture as suspended vapor. The full amount of water is therefore passed through the compressor. This warm air then cools in the receiver and in the air lines. When it reaches room temperature (90 deg F) it will be much more than saturated, and about 80% of the moisture will condense. This means that about 0.28 lb of water per minute, or two gal per hr will be deposited in the receiver and the air lines—enough to make the air really wet.[6]

Robert Nortier may have achieved the ultimate in farm electrification on his dairy and poultry farm near Rochester, N. Y.—and it's paying off.

"I use electricity because I can't depend upon a good supply of hired help," says Nortier. "I estimate my labor cost would be over $5,000 a

[5] French and Jarrett, *op. cit.*

[6] Gustafson, *op. cit.*

year. Contrast this with my present expenses—$475 for electricity for all farm operations. Interest and depreciation on an investment in equipment of $15,000 comes to $2,400 annually; say $300 for repairs; and you have a total yearly cost of about $3,200. Believe me, it's a lot more reliable than hired help!" [7]

Suppose you do not have even one case to cite. What then? Explain to the reader that no actual cases are now available, and go on to tell him what the results would be if an actual case were available. Set up a typical case for a mythical company, plant, city, or what have you. Then cite the savings, advantages, or other assets you are trying to explain. This method is almost as convincing as using actual cases.

Along with cases, or instead of them, you can use worked-out examples, showing the reader how to compute results, how to evaluate factors in a problem, or any of a number of other items you are discussing. Typical worked-out examples are given below:

System Design—Figure 9 shows a typical refinery piping system using slip joints, consisting of 8 inch steel pipe with a total length of 770 feet. It carries steam at 125 psig, with 25 F. superheat. The procedure for finding traverses, anchor loads, and guide and support locations is as follows:

Traverses: Saturation temperature for 125 psig. steam is 355 F. (Figure 7). Add 25 F. for a total temperature range (assuming minimum temperature to be 0 F.) of 380 F. Expansion for this range is 3.4 inches per 100 feet, from Figure 7.

Span $AB = 140$ feet; expansion $= (140)(3.4)/100 = 4.8$ inches. A single-end joint with an 8-inch traverse is suitable at Point A. Span BC is 90 feet long and has an expansion of 3.1 inches when figured as above. Hence, joint C is single-end with 4-inch traverse. Span CE is 430 feet long with 14.7 inches of expansion. A double-end joint with an 8 inch traverse at each end is suitable at D, the approximate mid-point. Span EF is 110 feet long with 3.7 inches of expansion for which a single-end 4-inch traverse joint will be adequate.[8]

Sizing the compressor. The following example illustrates a method of determining compressor size and receiver capacity:

[7] From Anonymous, Kwhrs Replace Man-hrs on an All-Electric Farm, *Electrical World*, Oct. 7, 1957.

[8] From K. S. Roberts, Expansion Joints—How to Select and Maintain Them, *Petroleum Refiner*, Jan., 1957.

Example. An installation consists of three sizable boilers. Each is fitted with 20 air-puff-type blowers, which operate intermittently over a carefully timed and automatically controlled cycle. The boiler also has 10 retracting blowers which, to avoid overheating, must blow continuously when in the high-temperature zone. Determine the compressor size and receiver capacity.

Solution. Each intermittent air-puff unit blows 10 times per cleaning cycle. Each blow, lasting one second, requires 100 cu ft of free air. Therefore, the total free-air requirement of the 20 puff-type blowers is 20,000 cu ft. Each of the 10 retractable blowers requires 2500 cu ft per min (cfm) of free air for a sustained period of six minutes, totaling 150,000 cu ft free air. Thus, total air requirement is 170,000 cu ft per cleaning cycle per boiler.

Each boiler is cleaned once every 8-hour shift. Consequently, one boiler must be cleaned every 2.66 hours. Thus the average capacity required of continuously operating compressors is 170,000 cu ft/(60 min × 2.66 hour) = 1065 cfm of free air.

Consider that a 500-psig storage system is desired. This system, with the compressor capacity, should be sufficiently large to meet the instantaneous air demands of the blowers without permitting pressure drop in the 250-psig. working receiver to exceed a few pounds. Maximum sustained air requirement is the 250 cfm of each retractable blower. This is equivalent to 15,000 cu ft of free air during the 6-min blowing period. During this period, the air compressor puts 6390 cu ft (= 1065 cfm × 6 min) of free air into the system. Thus the storage system must make available an extra 8610 cu ft for the 6-min blowing period.[9]

4. Use illustrations to tell your story. More and more, today, people shy away from words. So use illustrations instead of words wherever you can. Your reader will be more interested in the article, will give it greater attention, and will be more satisfied by the appearance of the article.

While you can use an illustration or two as part of your article lead, the bulk of your illustrations will relate to the body of your article. Therefore be sure to refer to your illustrations in the body of the article. Try to write the article so that you refer to an illustration every few paragraphs. This helps carry your reader's interest and adds

[9] From Compressed Air and Gas Institute, Picking Compressors for Air Soot Blowing, *Power*, Sept., 1956.

unity to your article. Here are some typical examples of the use of illustrations in articles:

Installation. Referring to Fig. [7-1], the required compressor accessories and their arrangement are quite conventional except for the addition of the working receiver and the reducing valve between the storage and working receivers. The usual advice applies to these accessories. A quality air filter should be used with large and direct piping between it and the

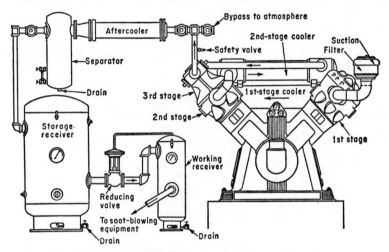

Fig. 7.1. Typical line illustration. (*Courtesy of Power*)

cylinder. If the filter is outdoors have it fitted with weather hood or louvers to keep out rain and snow. The aftercooler should be as close as possible to the compressor discharge to minimize the length of hot-discharge piping.[10]

Leadership is the art of getting things done through people. It is an art, not a science; it can be learned, but is hard to teach; it can be recognized, but is hard to measure.

The mechanics of management, of which leadership is the largest part, look something like this circle [Fig. 7-2].

1. As a manager, you receive instructions from, say, Head Office.

2. You work these into usable form for the men of your branch . . . you PLAN . . . then form your local, usable version of POLICY.

[10] *Ibid.*

3. You get action from your men . . . you secure execution.

4. You check to see that the execution was satisfactory; you learn to do better next time; you CONTROL.

Between these processes you are involved in a communication—you cannot do without it. Communication comes from a French word meaning "to share"—you can talk all you like but do not communicate unless you and the other man share your thoughts—your understandings. Communication really means transferring a thought or an idea from your

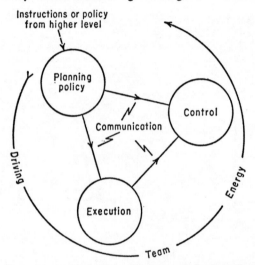

Fig. 7-2. Steps in communication. (*Courtesy of Product Engineering*)

mind to his in such a way that he shares the thought with you. You get better, more successful, action when you can get him to see the picture in your mind—when you can see the picture in his, as he sees it!

In its simplest form, it should look like this (top diagram, [Fig. 7-3]).

But put yourself in the transmitter's place and then cast your mind back. If you will be honest with yourself you will remember occasions when, just as the words left your mouth, you realized that wasn't just what you meant to say. Again, you may remember when you found that the other fellow didn't understand you, but after you had restated the thought, he caught on. Maybe you should have said it differently the first time.

This failure to translate your mental picture into words accurately occurs frequently without your being aware of it. In effect, we all have a "scrambler" between our original idea generator and our word selector.

Similarly, our listeners all have their own scramblers, and so the picture changes to the second diagram.

But this is only the beginning. The picture you actually form in your

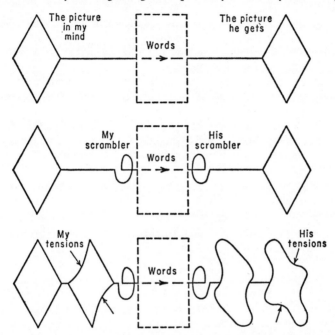

Fig. 7-3. Factors in communication. (*Courtesy of Product Engineering*)

mind is greatly affected by any surrounding tensions . . . by all the things that have ever happened to you . . . and especially by recent events. And when the receiver is an entirely different man operating under entirely different tensions, surroundings and feelings his picture (last diagram) really becomes distorted.

Now try constructing a diagram for two-way communication! What happens when the receiver merely tries to restate an idea back to the original transmitter? This, then, is our problem. We speak our thoughts inaccurately, the listener receives them even more inaccurately, and then he evaluates them in terms of what he feels and thinks. Subconsciously he asks, "What did he mean by those words?" Of course, this isn't the whole story. There are many other complications and problems involved, but basically, the answer is to practice putting yourself in the other fellow's shoes:

Concentrate on the thought he is trying to transmit. Try to see through his distortion.

Concentrate on his feelings; avoid thinking about your reaction to his words.

Restate his statement in your own words but in a form which he will accept as a true picture of what he thought.

When he does not appear to have received you clearly, try to find what actual picture he did receive, and why.

When you find two others having a problem in communication, try restating each man's point of view until each clearly understands the other's, even if he cannot accept it.

To the degree that others find you able to get a true picture of what they are thinking, they also will learn, and will try to share your thoughts. Now you are getting the benefits of two-way communication.[11]

5. Compare the old and the new. Readers understand contrast. Show them how the old plant or machine was inefficient and wasteful as compared with the new one. Every reader will understand immediately why you prefer the new to the old. Note how the following comparisons catch your interest.

A new cooling system will be used for the two main power transformers of Philadelphia Electric Co.'s new Eddystone Station. The system was designed by Allis-Chalmers Manufacturing Co. as a new approach to the safe overloading of transformers. It will enable one transformer to carry a good chunk of normal load of both transformers continuously if the other is disconnected for maintenance or repair. Forced-oil cooling is employed with banks of heat exchangers mounted away from the transformer tanks. Interconnecting pipes and valves make it possible to use all the heat exchangers to cool one of the transformers.[12]

Army Chemical Corps has just revealed that beta-propiolactone vapor is an excellent germ-killing agent for sterilizing hospital rooms and bacteriological laboratories. This discovery grew out of Chemical Corps research to develop defense techniques against biological warfare.

Other chemicals used for similar purposes are formaldehyde and ethylene oxide. The Army found beta-propiolactone to be several times faster

[11] From J. O. Dibbs, How to Make Instructions Clear, *Product Engineering*, Dec. 23, 1957.

[12] From Anonymous, New Cooling Hookup Lets One Transformer Carry 175% Load in Emergency, *Power*, Sept., 1956.

than formaldehyde, less irritating and more rapidly dissipated by simple airing. Ethylene oxide vapor, while showing many advantages as a sterilizing agent, is rather slow-acting and can thus tie up valuable space for too long a time. The Chemical Corps has used beta-propiolactone at Fort Detrick to disinfect entire laboratory buildings, keeping them out of operation only a day or so in the process.[13]

To prove our point, here's the case history of a firm who licked this problem with our key-sort cards. Let's meet B T Morgan Jr (author's note: no relative!), superintendent of Jackson Mills, No. 1, in Iva, South Carolina. His mill has used our cards for over two years.

"What has orderly scheduling done for you?" I asked my namesake. Morgan replied: "I don't know how we could operate without it, considering our expansion program. He then told how some of his men had voluntarily bought standard ledger books. By hand entries they tried to record and control the many maintenance jobs they had to do at times. "The human mind can't handle such a mass of details in that fashion," observed Morgan.

As an example, he mentioned the hundreds of motors in Jackson's No. 1 mill. We knew it would be impractical to oil all those motors on a regular 6-week schedule. Staggering the scheduling was the only answer. Morgan reported that Jackson's card-sort system turned up a high percentage of motors with bone-dry bearings—likely to burn out and cause a production stoppage.[14]

6. Cite advantages. Today's readers want to know how they will profit by using the methods or devices you suggest. While you can spend many pages telling them what the advantages are, a few examples will be far more convincing. So cite advantages and then use cases or examples to prove your statements. The body of your article will be much stronger if you use these methods to convince your readers. By citing several cases or examples you can often move the reader to investigate further. And this, after all, is the best proof that your article has helped the reader.

WRITE CLEARLY AND EFFECTIVELY

Up to now in this chapter we have discussed only the factual aspects of the body of your article. The reason for this is that your

[13] From C. H. Chilton, Chementator, *Chemical Engineering*, Mar. 24, 1958.
[14] From R. T. Morgan, Sure-Fire Maintenance Control, *Power*, Sept., 1956.

facts must be clear and presented to advantage if your reader is to profit from reading your article. But all the facts in the world will not convince your readers unless your presentation is clear and effective. Let's see how you can improve the readability of the body of your article.

Here are seven basic rules for making the body of your article easier to read: (1) Weed out abstract words; instead use concrete and familiar words. (2) Beware of pomposity. (3) Slash wordiness. (4) Interlock your ideas for unity and coherence. (5) Choose action verbs. (6) Give the right emphasis to your ideas. (7) Vary your style.

Abstract words. Here are eight abstract words: "alleviation," "attribution," "collusive," "equivocation," "inadmissible," "modicum," "nonpareil," and "subservience."

Try to define each of these words. You will find that it is extremely difficult to define most of these words in terms of concrete symbols. Abstract words like these bore a reader. Your reader must stop and mentally define each of these words as he reads it. The body of your article will move much faster and the reader will acquire more information if you use words that are familiar and easy to understand. Words that represent visible, tangible materials help you express your ideas clearly and quickly.

Of course, there will be many times when you cannot use a concrete word instead of an abstract one. But try to avoid the abstract word as much as possible.

Here are some typical examples of concrete words: "gasoline," "water," "wing," "magneto," "grease," and "rudder." Note how each of these words has a definite meaning when used in the body of your article. So be specific; use as many concrete words as possible, to help your reader.

Shun pomposity. Strive to express your ideas clearly. Never try to impress your reader with big words. For big words are often abstract, empty of real meaning, and confusing. The best way to impress your reader is to express your ideas so clearly that he understands them on the first reading. The reader will finish your article with the feeling that its author really knows his subject and knows how to express it in written words.

Pomposity can turn a reader against an author and his subject. If the reader does not feel at ease, he may give up in the middle of your article. And since this is where most of your important facts are located, you lose the full effect of your writing.

Slash wordiness. Be concise. Use as few words as possible to convey your ideas to the reader. Concise writing is usually better than wordy writing because it conserves the reader's time and energy. Make every word count when you write the body of your article, just as you do when you're sending a telegram.

Don't be afraid of using too few words. For if you find that the body of your article is too much like a skeleton, you can always expand your wording. This is much easier to do than cutting out words.

Interlock your ideas. Give unity and coherence to your article by relating one idea to another. By using subheads you can often bridge the gap between two or more ideas. Illustrations and tables are also useful in relating your ideas to one another. Several examples of how you can interlock ideas with subheads are given below. You will also find a number of examples in the excerpts given earlier in this chapter. Study all of these carefully. Note how boldface subheads are used.

Most of us can use more money these days. But more so than ever before, promotions are not handed to you because you're a nice fellow looking for one. Competition for advancement up the ladder of success is keener than ever.

Over the years, I have seen some men climb up the ladder of success and others slide down. I've analyzed both operations, and if you are interested in climbing higher or you are wondering why you're losing your grip on the success ladder, my notes may be valuable to you as they have been to me.

Let Others Do Things for You

Every man that I have studied on his way up was able to somehow get things done through people.

The knack of doing this is to work calmly—but calculatedly—to bring out the best in others without bringing yourself into their spotlight. If you do everything you can to help others get the credit, you never will have to worry about getting the credit yourself.

Use Both Your Ears

There's no better way to line people up behind you than by making solid friends out of them. And nobody has yet found a more reliable way of making friends than by stopping, looking and listening eagerly to people.

When people know their ideas are not going to be stolen, their minds work overtime to dig new ones up; and what boss is there who doesn't like to see his associates help him get a promotion?

The best way to get ahead in most cases still is to do everything you can to help your boss get a promotion. The more your boss comes to depend on you, the more indispensable you will be to him as he climbs the ladder of success.

Beware of Detailphobia

Some men give careful and competent attention to detail; but the person who is lost in a maze of details is doomed to mediocrity. Of course, certain matters of immediate moment require quick decisions followed by immediate action.

Show Obedience, Loyalty

Let your boss down, buck him, belittle him behind his back, or do something to make him feel you're not giving him the support he can rightfully expect of you, and you can be court-martialed just as decisively as you might for desertion while under fire and in uniform.

Ladder-climbing requires that you look at your superiors on the rungs above you as persons with more experience and training who you can respect and from whom you can learn. When they direct you to do something, you don't resent it; you go ahead and do it, figuring that they know more about it than you do.

Similarly, when you are criticized, take it on the chin, cheerfully and do not feel indignant nor injured. Take the attitude that your boss is calling attention to your mistakes because he is trying to train you to be more efficient on your job and more useful to him. If he did not think you were worth training, he wouldn't bother to criticize. He would get rid of you and try someone else.[15]

When you won't accept a new idea, be sure it's for logical reasons. Too often our first response is negative—on general principles—and our reactions are likely to be among the five standard ones listed below. They are usually preceded by:

"What good is it?"

The negative tone of voice is supposed to be crushing—but inventors

[15] From O. A. Battista, Six Sure Steps to the Top, *Chemical Engineering,* Feb. 24, 1958.

are just inconsiderate enough to have thought up some practical applications—or else, they smile and repeat what Michael Faraday was supposed to have said, "Some day, sir, you will tax it."

Next come the so-called professional opinions, but most often these are based on emotional rather than professional opinion. Here are the three examples and what they really mean.

"It Isn't Practical" (*claiming an empirical knowledge of evaluation*).

This roadblock might be expected to come from the uninitiated, but it is more frequently the expression of the expert. In order to understand the underlying meaning, it might be interpreted in several ways:

"It won't work—doesn't agree with an accepted principle."

"I haven't seen anyone making money with it."

"I can't organize it in my compartmental thinking."

"It has never been done that way, so, it won't work."

"I don't have a mathematical formula to explain it."

By giving the inventor's efforts a bit of faint praise the questioner is saying, "Now, I have done my part since I have admitted the obvious in a cautious sort of way but I don't see any reason to open the bulkheads of my compartmentalized, domain-oriented thinking.

"Instead, I will cause the originator to overreach himself trying to unscrew the inscrutable and then dismiss the whole affair as a poor sales effort. My mental living room is completely furnished; I don't need to buy anything new—it is comfortable just as it is."

As for the statement, "I haven't seen anyone making money with it," the answer must inevitably be, "Of course you haven't." What kind of comparison can be given an entirely new product? Only parents have the courage to give a glowing description of the newborn babe and its future possibilities. To the average individual the question, "What good is the baby?" has to be answered, "Wait and see."

"I Don't Have a Formula for It" (*demanding a mathematical precedent*).

Very likely true. It may require a number of formulas, in an original arrangement. Negative and positive catalysts may be involved. The originator probably doesn't have a formula either, but he is still a hundred light years and a million dollars ahead of the skeptical mathematician.

Neither Edison nor Bell advertised their products as being the results of mathematical exploration. But their work did open doors to many mathematical excursions.

"It Hasn't Been Done That Way—It Won't Work" (*demanding conformity*).

Edison said that his greatest worry in building the first power station was the engineers. They continually told him what couldn't be done until he decided that his guessing was better than their computations and he just went on guessing. And who would say at this point that they were not guessing too? [16]

Choose action verbs. Words like "turn," "push," "touch," "connect," "lift," "grind," and "cut" suggest action and movement. But words like "maintain," "exist," "remain," "evaporation," "acquisition," and "seem" are static. They do not stir the reader or interest him.

So whenever possible, choose active verbs. Your writing will move faster and you will need fewer words to tell your story. This is extremely important in the body of your article because it is here that the reader begins to tire.

Emphasize important ideas. Never leave your most important ideas out of the body of your article. Why? For this reason—your reader may never read beyond the start of the body of your article. He may tire, be interrupted, or have the habit of not reading beyond the first page of an article. If you leave your most important ideas for the end, this reader will never see them.

Try to arrange your ideas in an order of descending importance. Make your most important idea the first part of the body of your article. Follow this with the second most important idea. Continue this way until you reach the least important idea. This should be near the end of the body of your article.

This arrangement may seem to be extra work, but it gives you a better chance of having your most important ideas read. And this, after all, is why you are writing your article.

Vary your style. Don't try to put your readers to sleep. Vary the sentence and paragraph length in the body of your article. If all your sentences and paragraphs are about the same length the words have a lulling effect on the reader. He may begin to drowse.

When you use a long sentence—say twenty words or more—try to follow it with a short sentence. Do the same for paragraphs. But avoid choppiness. Sentences and paragraphs become choppy when one short sentence or paragraph follows immediately after another. Here is an example of a group of choppy sentences.

[16] From H. R. Johnson, Invisible Roadblocks to Invention, *Product Engineering*, Feb. 10, 1958.

First, take the plug from its socket. Measure the gap. Check for carbon deposits. Observe the wear of the points. Then clean it. Finally, replace it. Connect the lead wire. Work with each plug in this manner.

Note the stop-go, stop-go effect of this writing. If you want to express thoughts in a staccato way, list them as a series of steps with a number or letter in front of each. But if you do not want to make a list, then rewrite your sentences. The above instructions might be rewritten as:

To make sure that the cylinders are getting a spark, you should remove the plugs and examine each one closely; then you should clean them, set the gap, and replace them. But take one at a time. Otherwise, you may switch them and possibly delay the job of determining the weak cylinder.

Another way of varying your style is by personalizing your writing. Get your reader into the act. To do this, use personal and active words. Typical personal words are "you," your," "hold," "turn," and "write." These words imply that the reader actually takes part in the work or procedure you are describing. He can follow it much more easily when it is expressed in these terms.

Study the many examples of typical articles given in this chapter to see how their writers varied the style. And the next time you pick up a technical or business magazine, do the same. You will soon learn that all good writers vary the style of their writing whenever possible.

MAKE YOUR CONCLUSIONS CLEAR

Most business papers today do not give much space to conclusions at the end of their articles. The reason for this is that many editors prefer to state the essence of the article in the blurb, or lead paragraph of the article. But in your writing it is best to use a conclusion for your article. The conclusion rounds out your thinking. If the editor wants to transfer your conclusions to the blurb, it is easy for him to do this. Here are some hints on writing your conclusion.

Write your conclusion so it summarizes the body of your article. In a short article one sentence is enough as a conclusion. In longer articles you may need a paragraph or more. But no matter what length you choose, don't get windy. The place for details is in the body of your article.

94   *Successful Technical Writing*

So state your conclusion and stop. Be concise, specific, and clear. Your readers will appreciate the effort you devote to making your conclusion short and direct.

If you wish to include a bibliography or references for your article, insert them immediately after your conclusion. Then your readers can use this material or ignore it, depending upon their needs. Typical examples of conclusions for articles are given below. Note that some of these articles do not contain a bibliography or references.

When the separator is located at the outlet of the aftercooler, it may be overburdened, for it will have to remove all of the moisture. It is better practice to place it in the line from the air receiver. When this is done, much of the moisture will first drop out in the receiver, leaving less work for the separator. The result will be drier air.

The common, locally-made, water trap, simple baffle type, can be useful in long lines too.

By realizing these characteristics of compressed air, and by properly applying the drying techniques discussed here, it should be possible to eliminate costly water from practically any compressed air system.[17]

In the kilns, operating as high as 3,300 F., water is driven from the hydrate leaving the finished magnesia. Before entering kiln, magnesium hydroxide may be pepped up with finely divided silica as a sintering air to produce high quality product.

Kaiser operates three kilns in order to get a high degree of process flexibility and turn out several grades of magnesia.[18]

Regardless or whether a gas is ideal or not, the specific heat ratio C_p/C_v gives the ratio of the slope of the isentropic curve to that of the isothermal curve intersecting it at any given point on the P-V plane. As Edmister (4) points out, specific heat ratios of real gases have other applications as well.

REFERENCES

1. Budenholtzer, R. A., B. H. Sage and W. N. Lacey, *Ind. Eng. Chem.*, 31, 369 (1939).
2. De Laney, E. G., "Thesis in Chemical Engineering," Newark College of Engineering, Newark, N.J., 1955.

[17] Gustafson, *op. cit.*
[18] From Magnesia from Sea Via Streamlined Process, *Chemical Engineering*, Mar. 24, 1958.

3. Edmister, W. C., *Ind. Eng. Chem.*, 32, 373 (1940).
4. Edmister, W. C., *Petroleum Refiner*, 27, Nov., 1958.
5. Edmister, W. C., and R. J. McGarry, *Chem. Eng. Progress*, 45, 421 (1949).
6. Rossini, F. D., and others, "Selected Values of Physical and Thermodynamic Properties of Hydrocarbons and Related Compounds," Carnegie Press, 1953.
7. Sage, B. H., E. R. Kennedy and W. N. Lacey, *Ind. Eng. Chem.*, 28, 601 (1936).
8. Seifarth, J. H., and J. Joffe, *Ind. Eng. Chem.*, 44, 2894 (1952).
9. Sledjeski, E. W., *Ind. Eng. Chem.*, 43, 2913 (1951).
10. Weiss, A. H., and J. Joffe, *Ind. Eng. Chem.*, 49, 120 (1957).[19]

Remember, your conclusion offers you a rare opportunity to repeat the main points of your article. So be extremely careful to choose the best ideas for your conclusion. You will often find that the best conclusion is simply a restatement of the first or second sentence of your lead. In many articles you will be able to restate the ideas from your lead in fewer words than you used in the lead.

Since the end of your article is the last chance you will have of influencing your readers, write the conclusion so that your strongest point will be freshest in the reader's mind when he finishes your article.

In a long article—say six or eight published pages—your conclusion should be comprehensive. Summarize the main details of the article first. Then show how these details relate to one another. Your purpose here is to bring the entire article into clear focus. If the reader finishes with only a hazy notion of what you have said, your article has failed. But if your reader finishes the article with a clear idea of what you have said, your article has succeeded. Your conclusion can help you achieve this kind of clarity.

SUMMARY

A snappy lead gets your reader into the article. To hold the reader you must keep the body of your article interesting. To do this, be concise, stick to your outline, keep your story in mind, write a little each day, and finish soon. The body of your article will be stronger if you know your audience and purpose, develop your subject from the lead, cite cases and give examples, use illustrations, compare the new with the old, and cite advantages. To make the body of your

[19] J. Joffe and E. G. Delaney, Heat Capacity Ratios—5 Hydrocarbons, *Chemical Engineering*, Mar. 24, 1958.

article easier to read, weed out abstract words, do not be pompous or verbose, strive for unity, use action verbs, emphasize important ideas, and vary your style. For the final strengthening of your article, make your conclusion clear. Use as short a conclusion as possible. Then stop writing.

CHAPTER CHECK-UP

1. Why must the body of your article be interesting?
2. Give five rules for making the body of your article interesting.
3. Why should you write a little each day?
4. What advantage is there in finishing your writing job promptly?
5. Why should you know your audience and purpose in writing?
6. How can you develop the subject of your article from the lead?
7. Choose a technical magazine which interests you. Study its articles and select two of them in which cases are cited. Do these cases help you understand the subject better?
8. How can you compare the new with the old in an article?
9. Why should you cite advantages in an article?
10. Give seven rules for making your article easier to read.
11. What is an abstract word? Give five examples.
12. What is a concrete word? Give five examples.
13. How can you interlock the ideas in your article?
14. What is an action verb? Give five examples.
15. How can you emphasize important ideas in your article?
16. Why should you avoid choppy sentences?
17. Give three examples of how you can vary your style of writing.
18. What should the conclusion of your article contain? How long should your conclusion be?

Chapter 8

USE ILLUSTRATIONS AND TABLES

WHY ILLUSTRATIONS?

Today business papers use more illustrations than ever before in publishing history. Why? There are several excellent reasons: (1) Illustrations—photos or drawings—convey a message or idea faster than the printed word. (2) Many complex machines and circuits cannot be adequately described in words—illustration is necessary. (3) Readers usually find illustrated articles easier to read and give them more attention. (4) Good illustrations improve the appearance of a published article. (5) Editors have greater flexibility in planning the article layout when the author supplies good illustrations.

WHAT KINDS OF ILLUSTRATIONS?

You can use almost any kind of illustrations for your article. Photos, line drawings, graphs, charts, maps, business forms, and cartoons are frequently used in modern business papers. The choice rests with you. At times the editor may suggest what kinds of illustrations he thinks are best. Follow his suggestions if at all possible.

There are a number of pointers to keep in mind while choosing the illustrations for your article. Let's see what they are and how they will improve your writing effectiveness.

GET TOP MILEAGE FROM ILLUSTRATIONS

To get the best return from the time you devote to illustrations for your article:

1. Get the best illustrations possible.
2. Use a professional photographer or draftsman.
3. Use only those illustrations that help your story—reject others.
4. Send "atmosphere" shots as extras.
5. Follow the editor's instructions when preparing illustrations.

You may know of other useful rules. If so, add them to this list. But for now let's look closer at the above five.

1. Get the best quality. Editors will love you for it. And your acceptance batting average will soar. Besides, editors use more of the good illustrations. You'll find that either all or almost all the illustrations you submit will be published. So never skimp on illustration quality. You may save pennies but you're fooling only yourself.

2. Use a professional photographer or draftsman. This is the one sure way of getting quality illustrations. But after you hire a professional, don't desert him. Show him exactly what you want. If you're striving for a certain effect in a photo, tell him. Some effects are difficult to express in words. But try. A competent professional will read between the lines and come up with something close to what you want. And remember that the more photos he takes, the better your chances of getting something good.

Much the same applies to the draftsman. If you want some lines thicker than others, tell him. He'll work faster and more effectively. And you'll get the results you want, with fewer misunderstandings.

3. Use only illustrations that help your story. Make each illustration a nugget of valuable information. You save the reader's time and tell a better story. And you waste less time on illustrations the editor tosses out. So test each illustration by asking yourself: Can I tell the story without this? If the answer is yes, delete the illustration, no matter how fond of it you may be. This isn't alway easy, but you must do it if you want to use only the best.

4. Send atmosphere shots as extras. Editors like illustrations that set the scene for the reader. But sometimes there isn't enough space to use atmosphere shots. Submit them as extras that the editor can use or discard as he wishes, and you will give him greater flexibility in his layout of the article.

5. Follow the editor's instructions when preparing illustrations. Illustration needs and requirements vary from one business paper to the next. So ask the editor what he wants and prepare your illustrations to meet these needs. If you do, your article will be published sooner and with less trouble.

Some editors accept rough sketches for line illustrations. These are redrawn before publication. In such cases you need not have a draftsman make your drawings, as suggested above. But if you think you'll have any other use for the line drawings, as in catalogs, bulletins, or other company publications, it is wise to have the drawings made by a draftsman. Send the editor clean, sharp copies. Remember—never submit your illustrations and text separately—they're liable to be separated forever. Send the text and illustrations for your article *at the same time and in the same package.*

Mark your name and the figure number on the back of each illustration. Use a grease pencil for photos. All editors prefer that photos be 8- by 10-in. sharp glossies. Never type on the back of a photo—it shows through. Type a separate list of captions, using the figure numbers appearing on the illustrations.

PHOTOS CAN TELL YOUR STORY

Modern business papers and technical magazines devote almost as much space to illustrations as they do to text. And it looks as though the trend to greater use of illustrations will continue to grow. So learn now to use photos wisely.

Photos find two primary uses in articles: (1) as the principal elements of a picture story, and (2) as supporting elements in a story containing a relatively large amount of text. Let's look first at picture stories, to see how you can use photos as the basis of an article.

PICTURE STORIES

In this kind of article you use photos to tell your story. If necessary, one or more drawings may also be used. The only text needed is a short introduction, plus a caption for each illustration. Since the text is relatively short, you must see that captions are terse and to the point. Most business papers limit caption length to four lines. Keep this in mind when writing your photo captions.

Don't try to write your captions so that they exactly fit the space you think the editor will give them. This is the editor's job. And he can do it better and faster than you ever could. Instead, phrase your captions to include all the essential information the reader needs. But keep them short.

Picture stories can be used for almost all the twelve kinds of articles we discussed in Chapter 2. For best results, look for step-by-step processes—they make the best picture stories. Here are four rules to help you get better illustrations for picture stories:

1. Try to use people in action in each photo.
2. Concentrate on the article subject.
3. Boost effectiveness with close-ups.
4. Crop for drama.

You can summarize these rules in four key words—*action, concentration, detail,* and *selection.* Here's how to apply the rules.

1. Use people in action. Photos of machines are seldom interesting unless related to some human activity. So if you want to show a lathe, don't photograph it just standing in the shop. Have a machinist operate the lathe—then snap your photo. When posing the person in the picture, get him to relax before you snap the shutter. This is one more argument for using a professional photographer—your photos will have far better composition. The professional knows how to make people relax and how to make them unobtrusive in the photo.

2. Concentrate on the article subject. Let's say your article deals with only the chuck of the lathe. Then concentrate on it. Don't show a picture of the entire lathe—the chuck may not even be visible. Build all your photos around the chuck. Show the machinist adjusting the chuck, or doing some routine task with it. Only the man's hands need be shown—don't split the reader's interest by showing the man's face. Remember—as human beings we are primarily interested in other people. If you show a person's face in a photo the reader is almost certain to look at the face before he looks at the equipment in the photo.

Of course, you can't always concentrate on a relatively small part of the equipment, showing only hands near it. With some equipment, for example, calculators, fork-lift trucks, and elevators, you must show the operator sitting or standing at his normal place. You can avoid excessive interest in the operator by having him dressed in working clothes, stationed so he is partially turned away from the camera. Once again, a professional photographer is your best source of help.

Have all persons appearing in your photos sign a release authorizing you to use the photo for publication. A typical release form is shown below.[1]

Date....................19....

I am of legal age, and in consideration of......................., the receipt of which I hereby acknowledge, I hereby sell and assign (YOUR NAME), his customers and agents, the exclusive right to copy and reproduce the photographs of me, taken by (YOUR NAME) in any manner whatsoever, and to secure copyright for all such reproductions.

.... (Model's signature)
.... (Witness)

3. Boost effectiveness with close-ups. An over-all view of a machine gives the reader a good idea of your general subject. But to really put your point across, spotlight his attention with one or more close-ups. Returning to the lathe example, your over-all shot might show the chuck and its relation to the rest of the lathe. With a few close-ups you could show the jaws of the chuck, any special design features about them, and their opened and closed positions. Such a series of photos would really show your reader the important details of the chuck. And remember—your ultimate purpose is to serve the reader. Keep this in mind and the quality of your illustrations will soar.

4. Crop for drama. At times you'll take a photo that has one part of major interest—the rest is almost worthless. What to do? Crop. Crop the photo so that only the interesting portion is shown. Have a print made of just this part. The results will delight you. Why? Because you've applied rules 2 and 3—concentration and detail. So remember the cropping rule. It will produce effective results almost every time.

What you might call "cropping-in-reverse" is another technique. Here you take a photo and study it for the most interesting parts. These parts are then enlarged to standard 8 by 10 glossies. If the

[1] Eugene Wyble, "Sell Your Photographs," American Photographic Publishing Co., Boston, Mass., 1942.

editor is agreeable, you can indicate what parts of a photo are the most interesting. Then he can have them enlarged when the halftone engraving is made. But it's better to have the enlarging done yourself, if at all possible. That way you are in a position to control the results, because you see the photo before submitting it.

TEXT-TYPE ARTICLES

In this type of article you use photos as supporting elements for the text. The photos illustrate the points you discuss in the text.

Use the same rules for the text-type article as for the picture story. Just because your story is mostly text is no reason for slighting the illustrations. Good illustrations make good text material better. Why? Because your readers get your ideas faster and enjoy seeing how well they are illustrated. So remember the rules—*action, concentration, detail,* and *selection.*

WORK FROM THE OUTSIDE IN

Study a number of well-illustrated articles in modern business papers and you'll note one common trend in photo selection. Editors like to work from the outside in. Thus in a plant story the first photo is almost always an exterior view of the new plant. The next shot usually shows an over-all view of the plant interior. Photos that follow show details of the interior and the equipment in the plant. Such an arrangement makes sense because you see the plant in about the same sequence as if you personally visited it.

The same general principle is used with machines, electronic equipment, and other devices in which both the exterior and the interior interest the reader.

So use this principle when planning your photos. Start with an over-all view and work inward. Such a scheme usually works out well with the text outline because, as you learned in Chapter 4, the usual article begins with an over-all description. Then it moves to specific details. Remember that in an article dealing with only one part of a machine the over-all view would be of just this part, unless you feel that a view of the entire machine would help the reader.

Photos can carry a major portion of an article's picture load. But often a photo falls short in one or more respects because it can't show us details a drawing can. You'll find that in almost every article you'll want to use both photos and line drawings. Let's see how to plan for and use line drawings.

SAVE WORDS—SAY IT WITH DRAWINGS

Engineers use hundreds of drawings in the manufacture, testing, and operation of complex machines and devices. Many of these drawings make good illustrations for technical articles. You can say that almost any good drawing can be converted to article use, if there are no security obstacles. Military security regulations and company rules sometimes prevent use of certain drawings for publication. So check the security status of each drawing you intend to use *before* submitting it. Then there's no chance of having to recall an illustration.

About ten common types of drawings are widely used in business papers today:

1. Shop drawings or blueprints for building a part or a machine
2. Assembly drawings showing a complete machine and its parts
3. Patent drawings used to record pertinent design features
4. Plot plans and maps showing land and water areas
5. Architectural and structural detail drawings
6. Schematic drawings prepared to simplify complex details
7. Pictorial drawings—perspective or some form of isometric
8. Renderings of the exterior or interior of a part or machine
9. Piping drawings for pressure piping, plumbing, and other lines
10. Flow or organization charts or drawings for plants or materials

CHOOSING YOUR DRAWINGS

Your first question when thinking of an illustration should be: Shall I use a photo or a drawing, or both? Usually photos are better for exterior and interior views where the dimensions and certain details of the part are not of too much importance to the reader. But when you wish to show how a part, or an entire machine, is made or what the dimensions of various parts are and how they are fastened, use a drawing. With a drawing you can show hidden parts that would be invisible in a photo. Choose a drawing instead of a photo if you want to show dimensions, materials, fastenings, joints, hidden parts, flow of materials, schematic assemblies, and any other important details.

When you think that it is important to put the reader into the area illustrated by a drawing, or that it would help him to see the part as it actually is, use both a drawing and a photo. The drawing shows the reader the construction or other details, while the photo makes it easier for him to understand what the part or machine is actually like.

One of the big advantages of a drawing is that you can control what it shows; with a photo you must accept what the camera sees. You can control the drawing by showing the reader only those parts you are discussing in the text. Thus you focus his attention on the important items. This can't be done as readily with a photo, particularly if there are hidden parts.

So to choose the best drawings for your article, think of the reader. Ask yourself: What am I trying to get across? Your answer will almost always supply the key to the best drawing.

Let's say you want to show the site of a new plant and how the plant was located to take advantage of the terrain and the water supply of a nearby river. Ask yourself: What do I want to show? The answer here has three key words—*site, terrain, water.* Probably the best way of showing all three in a single illustration is by a drawing. And the kind of drawing that can include these features is a plot plan or map. Get out and study an example of each.

Ask yourself another question: What parts of this drawing are important to the reader? Usually you'll find that the reader needs only about half the information in the typical engineering drawing. So start crossing out the useless information on the drawing. On a plot plan you may delete items like angles between boundary lines, names of adjacent property owners, over-all dimensions of the plot, street names, town and city names, elevations, and survey dates. If any of these is essential to your article, leave them on the drawing, of course. But the simpler your drawing, the faster the reader can understand it. Figure 8-1 shows a typical example of a plot plan used in a magazine article. Note how it was prepared to give only the essential information needed by the reader.

Machine drawings need even more simplification than plot plans and maps. The usual machine drawing used in industry contains a large number of lines and notes (see Fig. 8-2a). Simplified for magazine use, the drawing contains many fewer lines and notes (see Fig.

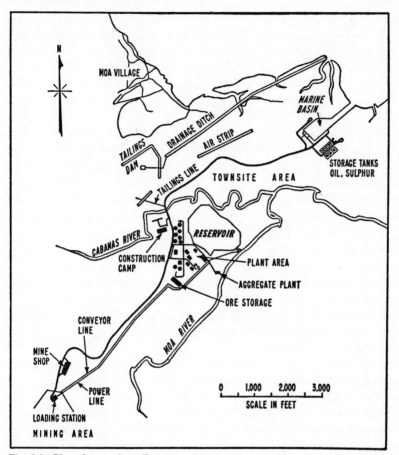

Fig. 8-1. Plot plan used to illustrate a business-paper article. (*Courtesy of Engineering and Mining Journal*)

8-2*b*). In your industrial drawing you are trying to tell someone how to build a machine or how it is built. But in your technical article you never have enough space to describe every detail of construction. Hence the drawing can be simplified.

Blueprints and other kinds of industrial drawings can be made extremely large if necessary. But the average business paper has a page of limited size. To show in a magazine illustration every line and note that appears on an industrial drawing is impossible. The page would

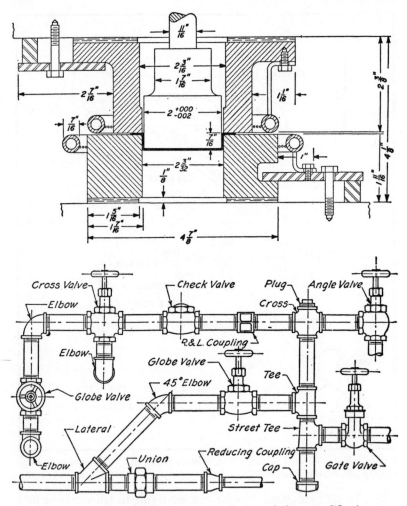

Fig. 8-2. (*a*) Two typical engineering drawings before simplification.

be so cluttered with lines and lettering that it might look like one big splotch of ink and be unattractive to the eye. Any drawing of a large machine that you plan to use in your article should be simplified as much as possible. For if you don't do it, the editor will—or he'll toss out the illustration.

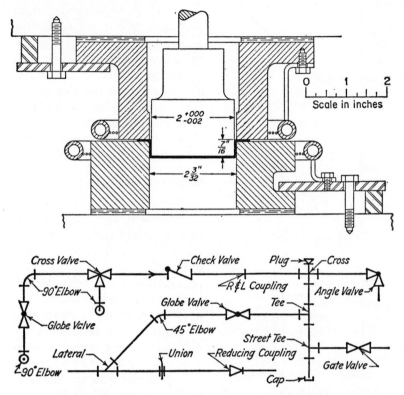

Fig. 8-2. (*b*) The same drawings after simplification.

So your two key jobs in choosing drawings are: (1) Select the drawing that is best for your readers. (2) Simplify it so that you spotlight what he needs to know. Keep these in mind and you'll seldom go wrong.

And don't forget—professional draftsmen can do the best job of preparing illustrations from rough copy. If the editor you're working with wants finished drawings, hire a draftsman. You'll profit many times over.

CHARTS AND GRAPHS

Charts and graphs might also be called drawings because they're **made with** pen or pencil. But they require so much special thought

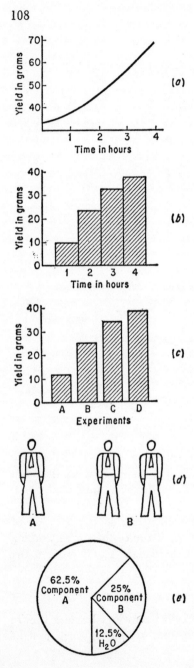

and care that we'll consider them separately. When you realize the many factors that you should consider, you'll agree that charts and graphs rate as much attention as any drawing of a machine part or circuit. You can use the following recommendations for preparing charts and graphs for articles, technical papers, lantern slides, etc.

SIX WAYS TO PRESENT
MATHEMATICAL DATA

When you have mathematical data to present you can use (1) a graph, (2) a histogram, (3) a bar chart, (4) a symbol chart, (5) a pie chart, or (6) a table. Which you choose depends on the data and what you're trying to show. Let's see when each should be used.

1. Graph. Use a graph when you want to show the relation between two quantities with a continuous curve (see Fig. 8-3a). You have a continuous relation between two quantities when you can secure a set of two values, one for each quantity, over a period of time, a distance, a speed, etc. You must have at least three points to obtain a curve, two for a straight line. The two quantities plotted are called variables.

2. Histogram. Use a histogram when you show a continuous func-

Fig. 8-3. Five ways of presenting data. (*Courtesy of E. I. Du Pont de Nemours & Co.*)

tion of a variable but do not have sufficient data to plot a continuous curve. Figure 8-3*b* shows a typical histogram.

3. *Bar chart.* Use a bar chart to compare data that are not a continuous function of some variable. Note that in a bar chart (Fig. 8-3*c*), there is a space between the bars; in a histogram there is no space between the bars.

4. *Symbol chart.* Use a symbol chart to compare data that are not a continuous function of some variable but lend themselves to some kind of pictorial representation (Fig. 8-3*d*). Use caution when planning symbol charts because the symbols can be misleading.

5. *Pie chart.* A pie chart (Fig. 8-3*e*) is useful when you wish to show the parts that make up the whole of something.

6. *Table.* A table is useful when you must present extensive data obtained under different conditions. Always arrange the table so the index column, or the value with which you enter the table, is in the first or left-hand column. When the table has a large number of columns, you can help the reader by repeating the index column on the right-hand side.

Now let's examine each of these means to present data a little more closely. You'll see there are many ways of improving the illustrations for your articles.

GRAPHS

A graph (Fig. 8-4*a*) is used, as you saw earlier, to show a continuous function of a variable when you have enough values to plot a continuous curve. Place the independent variable on the horizontal axis and the dependent variable on the vertical axis as in Fig. 8-4*b*. Intervals of time are usually placed on the horizontal axis.

Don't use too many curves on the graph (Fig. 8-4*c*). The fewer the curves on your graph, the quicker your reader will understand them. Some people feel that no more than three curves should be used on one graph. They recommend that if you must use more than three curves you should try to break the graph into a series of charts, each showing only a few curves (Fig. 8-4*d*). You can, if you wish, show the series of curves first, then the multicurve graph, which now serves as a summary for the viewer. The choice of the number of curves for a graph often depends on the space available for the illustration.

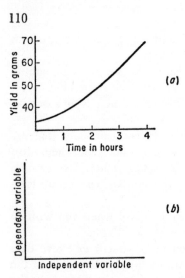

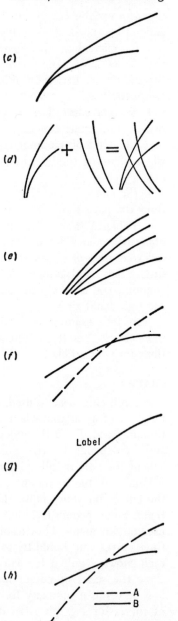

When you are trying to show your viewer general trends, plot only the typical curve of a family of curves. The typical curve shows the general trend (Fig. 8-4e) without confusing the viewer.

If the curves in your graph partly coincide, use different symbols for each (Fig. 8-4f). If you use symbols, remember that a solid line looks more important than a line of dashes. Likewise, a line of dashes looks more important than a line of dots. So be careful—don't let the symbols change the meaning of your graph.

Be certain that the curves are made *visibly* wider than the other lines on the graph. Make your curve labels short and simple (Fig. 8-4g).

Fig. 8-4. Be sure your charts are clear and easy to read. (*Courtesy of E. I. du Pont de Nemours & Co.*)

Keep all labels horizontal, if possible. Labels printed along the curve itself are often difficult to read.

Avoid using legends (Fig. 8-4*h*) to identify the curves in your article. A curve label is understood more easily and rapidly.

Data points (Fig. 8-5*a*) distract the attention of your viewer. So don't show data points merely to indicate you plotted the curve correctly. But if the curve's location is more important than its general shape, and if you discuss its location, then include the data points. Make them closed circles or triangles which are no smaller than the smallest letters in your illustration.

Avoid the use of fine grids for all graphs to be used for publication or in slides for presentation before an audience. Heavy grids (Fig. 8-5*b*) distract from the curves. A skeleton grid, limited to the absolutely essential lines, is preferred (Fig. 8-5*c*). When the grid is not used, short stubs (Fig. 8-5*d*) are placed along both axes to indicate the scales.

When you eliminate the grid, you may prefer to use only one vertical axis line and one horizontal axis line. This emphasizes the shapes of the curves (Fig. 8-5*e*). The simplicity of the unframed grid can make a graph unusually effective.

Or you may prefer the framed graph (Fig. 8-5*f*). It tends to emphasize the importance of the scale values. Some curves look lost in a framed grid—others look awkward in an unframed grid. The final choice between a frame or no frame depends on your personal preference and the relative clarity of each for your readers or viewers.

The impression created by your graph depends on your choice of scales. Beware of the effect on your viewer. By expanding or shrinking the vertical scale (Fig. 8-5*g*) you can make the rate of change appear great or small; a steep curve seems to show a rapidly changing dependent variable, and a flat curve seems to show the opposite.

You can help the viewer of your graph by choosing the best scale graduations. Scales are easy to understand when they are graduated and numbered in 1, 2, or 5 units of measurement (multiplied or divided by 1, 10, 100, etc.). Chief exceptions you should make to this rule are time (days, months, years, etc.), probability, and similar irregular scales. Figure 8-6*a* shows a typical easily read scale.

Keep your scale captions (Fig. 8-6*b*) simple. Use key words for them, not complete sentences. Scale captions should always show

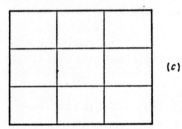

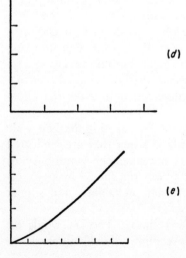

what is measured *and* the unit of measurement. Remember, the graph is useless unless your reader knows the unit of measurement— a load in pounds, time in hours, pressure in pounds per square inch, etc.

Avoid placing a power-of-10 factor in your scale captions. It is difficult for your viewer to tell if the scale values *are to be* or *have been* multiplied. Instead, place the power-of-10 factor at the beginning of the scale numbers (Fig. 8-6c). And, if possible, avoid large numbers on your horizontal scales (Fig. 8-6d).

You'll find that the scale caption for the vertical axis is usually lettered parallel to the axis. This

Fig. 8-5. Careful selection of chart grids is important. (*Courtesy of E. I. du Pont de Nemours & Co.*)

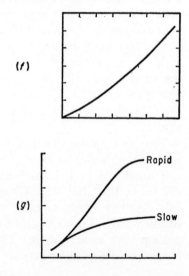

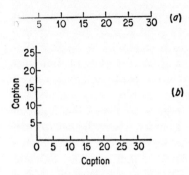

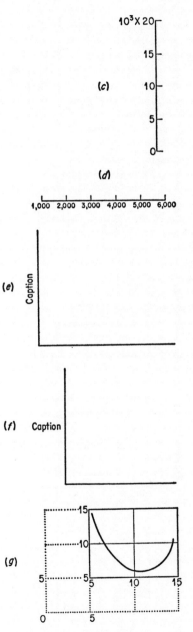

is not an ideal reading position, but it is satisfactory if the lettering is well done and the scale caption is simple and clear. The lettering should always read from the bottom of your graph to the top (Fig. 8-6*e*).

A horizontal-scale caption (Fig. 8-6*f*) is usually easier to read. But use this type carefully, because it can make the illustration look unbalanced and can attract too much attention. Also, the horizontal-scale caption wastes space, particularly if the words in it are long.

If the zero point of your scale is unimportant, omit it. By doing this you can often have a better-plotted curve and a better-balanced chart (Fig. 8-6*g*).

HISTOGRAMS AND BAR CHARTS

You can use both histograms and bar charts in about the same

Fig. 8-6. Choose your grid scales so they are easy to read. (*Courtesy of E. I. du Pont de Nemours & Co.*)

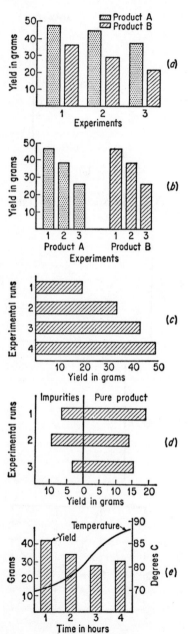

way—provided you remember the histogram is used for a continuous function of a variable. Bar charts are for plots of data that are not a continuous function of some variable.

Figure 8-7 shows five kinds of bar charts. Two schemes for presenting two series of data by bar charts are shown in Figs. 8-7a and 8-7b. (Figure 8-3c shows a bar chart presenting a single series of data.)

Most bar charts can be either horizontal or vertical. The arrangement you choose depends on what is best for your reader or viewer. Two horizontal bar charts are shown in Figs. 8-7c and 8-7d. When there is a range in values on either side of a zero point, use the

Fig. 8-7. Bar and symbol charts. (*Courtesy of E. I. du Pont de Nemours & Co.*)

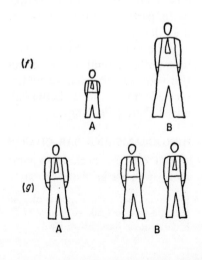

bilateral chart (Fig. 8-7d). If you wish, you can combine a bar chart and graph (Fig. 8-7e). Since the graph represents a continuous function, a combined bar chart and graph is the same as a combined bar chart and histogram. But the result is usually clearer when a graph is combined with a bar chart than when a histogram is.

SYMBOL CHARTS AND PIE CHARTS

Symbol charts and pie charts are most effective when comparing startling differences—the number of bathtubs in 1960 compared to the number of bathtubs in 1600. Symbol charts do not show comparisons as accurately as bar charts. When using a symbol chart, try to show only whole numbers. Select your symbols carefully; the wrong symbols can easily detract from the meaning of your chart.

Let's say you wish to show that one man weighs twice as much as another. Drawing the heavier man so he is twice as tall as the lighter man (Fig. 8-7f) is incorrect. Why? A man twice as tall as another man may weigh up to eight times as much as the smaller man. So choose your symbols as in Fig. 8-7g. This shows that the weight of one man is twice that of another.

When using pie charts remember that the parts must add up to unity, 100, or some other whole number. You may overlook this when rounding off numbers to make the chart easier for your reader to understand. If your parts do not add up to the whole, your reader may think you have purposely omitted some portion. So always check this point before having a pie chart prepared.

TABLES

While tables are not illustrations, many editors use tables as quasi-illustrations in their article layouts. So if you regard tables as having some of the characteristics of illustrations, you will get better results.

Six useful rules in preparing tables are: (1) Condense your data before tabulating it so the table will be as short as possible. (2) Use tables only where they are absolutely needed. (3) Keep all tables as simple as possible by reducing to a minimum the number of entries and columns. (4) Refer to the tables in the text of your article so the reader understands their purpose. (5) Show how your reader can apply the tabulated values—illustrative problems serve well for this. (6) Do not try to include complete lengthy tables; instead, extract a few typical values and use these in your illustrative examples and explanations.

Chapter 10 also gives many suggestions for simplifying tabular material. The following hints are based on recommendations of the American Society of Mechanical Engineers.

Where large numbers are to be included in a table, put them in terms of thousands, millions, etc., with the proper notation in the column heading. Sometimes you may be able to use larger units of measure, such as kilowatts, megawatts, and kilograms, to reduce the number of digits in the number. Where you do not need a high degree of accuracy, and especially where the accuracy of your numbers cannot be verified, it is better to round off large numbers. Thus, in place of tabulating a stress of 88,389 pounds per square inch, use 88,400, unless you actually compute the value to five or more significant figures.

Use special care with decimal quantities. The number 1.3 is not the same as 1.30 or 1.300. A measurement of 1.3 indicates an accuracy to the nearest tenth; 1.30 indicates accuracy to the nearest hundredth. You'll find that typists often add ciphers to give a uniform width to a column of decimal figures. Check all typed copy to avoid misleading your readers. For accuracy, use a cipher before the decimal points in all numbers having a value of less than unity. When tabulating long columns of figures, divide them horizontally into groups of five or ten to make reading easier.

NOMOGRAMS

Help the users of your nomograms—give a typical solution on each chart (Fig. 2-1). If possible, include a typical example *on* the chart. Then your reader need not refer to the text describing the chart when he is using it. Tell the editor to whom you submit your chart that you want both the solution line and example text on the chart— most editors will honor your request, if they have enough space on the chart.

LETTERING ON ILLUSTRATIONS

Check with the editor to find out what his lettering needs are. Some business papers redraw and reletter all illustrations—with these all you need to do is submit legibly lettered illustrations. It makes no difference if the lettering is freehand because the editor will have his illustration staff produce finished lettering suitable for reproduction.

But if the magazine to which you are submitting your article wants finished drawings, use machine lettering. Both the Leroy and Wrico Guides, as well as others, produce lettering satisfactory for reproduction. Have a professional draftsman do the lettering for you.

Most business papers use illustrations of four different widths— $2\frac{1}{8}$, $3\frac{1}{4}$, $4\frac{1}{2}$, and $6\frac{3}{4}$ in. The first two are probably the most popular, but the others find much use where wide illustrations are used. So when you are having machine lettering done, try to visualize the printed width of your illustrations.

To be legible, the reduced size of the lettering after reproduction should not be less than $\frac{1}{16}$ in. So an original drawing which is $8\frac{1}{2}$ by 11 in. should have lettering about $\frac{3}{16}$ in. high if the reproduction is to be $3\frac{1}{4}$ in. wide. Lettering on drawings of larger or smaller size should be sized so the reduced height is not less than $\frac{1}{16}$ in. Some business papers prefer larger lettering—up to about $\frac{1}{8}$ in. high.

MAKE YOUR ILLUSTRATIONS WORK

There is more to using illustrations than just choosing the most effective ones. To give your reader the maximum benefit of the illustrations, make your illustrations work. Here's how.

If possible, refer to every illustration in the text. Weave your text around the illustrations. Then the reader will refer back and forth, between text and illustrations. Never discuss something in the article text without referring to the appropriate illustration, if one is used. While you need not refer to numbered illustrations in exact arithmetical number, it is best to do so, if you can.

In studying the article outlines in Chapter 4 you will note that many of the 12 types can be built around a series of illustrations. Probably the most effective articles written today are those whose text revolves around a series of illustrations. Keep this in mind when outlining and planning your articles. An article in which the text and illustrations work together has a unity that appeals to all readers. So choose the best illustrations and put them to work.

WRITE CAPTIONS RIGHT

Illustration captions or legends tell your reader what illustration he is looking at. Captions also explain what the illustration is. To write captions right: (1) Study the magazine's caption style—pattern your captions after this style. (2) Keep your captions active and meaningful. (3) Be specific—generalized captions waste the reader's time and editor's space. (4) Keep your captions short and to the point—never allow a caption to run longer than three typewritten lines on standard 8½- by 11-in. typing paper.

1. Caption style. Some magazines begin their captions with the figure number; others end their caption with the figure number. The word "Figure" is used by some, others abbreviate it to "Fig." Or the word may not be used at all, but only a number. So study the magazine's captions and type yours to suit.

2. Keep captions active and meaningful. Compare these two typical captions:

Fig. 1: The room thermostat actuates the starter switch.
Fig. 1: The starter switch is actuated by the room thermostat.

The first caption is short, active, telling its story with few words. The second caption is passive, needs two more words. And the idea it presents does not reach the reader's mind as easily and quickly. So use active verbs instead of passive. Your reader will benefit more than you know.

Now compare two more typical captions:

Fig. 1: General view showing plant.
Fig. 1: New sewage plant handles 3,500 lb per day at a saving of $450 per day.

The first caption is hardly worth the words in it. Why? It tells the reader too little. But the second tells him what he sees. Keep every caption meaningful. You give your reader a major assist by packing every caption with facts. Well-written articles often tell enough of the story in the illustration captions to enable the reader to decide if reading the text would be worth his time. Remember—every article you write is competing for the reader's time. So make your captions worth the time it takes to read them.

CARTOONS CAN HELP YOUR STORY

In recent years business-paper articles have become less formal—human aspects of various fields are now treated in almost every issue of every magazine. So you'll find greater use of cartoons and similar illustrations.

Cartoons for business articles usually deal with an industrial situation (Fig. 8-8). Instead of carrying the normal caption used in humorous cartoons, the business-paper cartoon may combine the caption with the title of the article or the portion of the article in which the cartoon is used. See Fig. 8-8.

When planning cartoons for your articles keep these facts in mind: (1) Business-paper cartoons for articles are designed first for the point to be made, second for humor. So choose the intent of the cartoon, then bring in the humor. (2) Many cartoons used in articles have little humor—instead they convey an idea in a quick and easily understood way. (3) Be extremely careful not to offend your reader by underestimating his intelligence or knowledge of his field.

Check with the editor before submitting cartoons or similar illustrations. He'll advise you if the drawings should be rough or finished. And before beginning work on any cartoons study the tone and treatment the editor prefers.

HOW AND WHERE TO GET ARTICLE ILLUSTRATIONS

Look around you today—you're certain to find at least four good sources of illustrations almost immediately. Typical sources in industrial firms include (1) manufacturing and assembly drawings, (2) product sketches, (3) catalog illustrations, and (4) advertising photos and drawings.

When you can't obtain the illustrations you need, arrange to have photos taken or drawings made. Although there may be some expense for these, you can easily justify it by the use the illustrations may have. Besides using them in your article you can use the illustrations in catalogs, advertisements, operating and maintenance instructions, and technical papers.

THE MAN WHO WANTS OUT

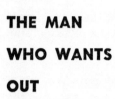

Sometimes you discover during an interview that a man wants to quit. This can be a serious problem, especially if he's a man you want to keep.

Suggestion—Find out why he wants to quit. Maybe all he needs is a chance to get a few things off his chest. On the other hand, if he has a valid complaint, perhaps you can correct it. Don't be afraid to tell him that you want him to stay. Some employees talk about leaving the company only because they're not sure they're wanted or where they stand.

THE QUICK-YES MAN

Some men agree quickly to avoid emphasis on the need for improvements. Some do it to avoid criticism.

Suggestion—First make sure your man's agreement is sincere. If so, strongly emphasize what he must do to improve. You'll probably need to make direct suggestions about improvement steps. Outline how you intend to follow up on these improvement plans. This close attention may be the very thing he needs.

CONFIRMED SUSPICIONS

It's long been believed that an employee's accident record is a direct reflection of his attitude toward safety. Now a study of 769 male employees from 54 industrial organizations proves this true. What's more, a complementary study of 481 supervisors shows that a supervisor's attitude toward safety has a direct bearing on his employees' safety record.

Dr. Earle Hannaford conducted the studies at New York University's Center for Safety Education. He concludes that money and effort spent in developing and maintaining good safety attitudes are amply justified. And that the use of safety record as a measure of supervisory performance is sound.

Fig. 8-8. Cartoons can help your article. (*Courtesy of Factory Management and Maintenance*)

HELPFUL AMERICAN STANDARDS

Listed below are 21 American Standards useful in preparing illustrations and text for articles and papers. All these standards can be obtained at nominal cost from the American Standards Association.

Abbreviations for Scientific and Engineering Terms, Z10.1
Abbreviations for Use on Drawings, Z32.13
Drawings and Drafting Room Practice, Z14.1
Graphical Symbols for
   Welding, and Instructions for Their Use, Z32.2.1
   Plumbing, Z32.2.2

Pipe Fittings, Valves, and Piping, Z32.2.3
Heating, Ventilating, and Air Conditioning, Z32.2.4
Railroad Use, Z32.2.5
Heat-power Apparatus, Z32.2.6
Letter Symbols for
Hydraulics, Z10.2
Mechanics of Solid Bodies, Z10.3
Structural Analysis, Z10.8
Heat and Thermodynamics, Including Heat Flow, Z10.4
Physics, Z10.6
Aeronautical Sciences, Y10.7
Radio, Y10.9
Meteorology, Y10.10
Acoustics, Y10.11
Chemical Engineering, Y10.12
Time-series Charts, Z15.2
General Guide:
A Guide for Preparing Technical Illustrations for
Publications and Projections [Proposed American Standard]

SUMMARY

Illustrations often mean the difference between acceptance and rejection of an article. But more important, they help you tell your story better. Your reader learns faster, more easily, more effectively. So choose your illustrations carefully. Try to get just the right photo or drawing each time. Your efforts will show every time—the article will get better readership. Once you choose the best illustrations, make them work for you. Give them good, crisp captions that are active and specific.

CHAPTER CHECK-UP

1. Give five reasons for using illustrations in technical articles.
2. What kinds of illustration can you use for your articles?
3. How can you get the most from your illustrations?
4. Give four rules for better illustrations for picture stories.
5. How would you choose illustrations for a text-type article?
6. When should you "work from the outside"?
7. How do drawings save words?
8. Describe how you would choose and simplify drawings for an article on a new machine tool.

9. Give six ways to present data to your reader. When should each be used?
10. Discuss graphs and their preparation.
11. How can you use histograms and bar charts?
12. Show how you can use symbol and pie charts. What precautions must you take with symbol charts?
13. What are six rules to observe when planning tables?
14. How should values be entered in tables when they are (*a*) decimal numbers, (*b*) numbers having six significant figures?
15. How should lettering be prepared for illustrations that are reproduced without being redrawn?
16. What is the smallest allowable size for lettering in printed illustrations?
17. Describe three ways to make illustrations work for you.
18. Write six active and specific captions. Why are they better than passive captions?
19. How can you use cartoons in your article? What must a cartoon do to be effective?
20. Where could you obtain illustrations in your company? What other sources are there for good illustrations?

Chapter 9

POLISH AND SUBMIT YOUR ARTICLE

Technical and scientific personnel meet two major troubles when writing. Either they (1) write too slowly, trying to revise as they write, or (2) do not spend enough time on revising their material after it is written. Both these troubles can cause many disappointments. Can they be avoided? Yes, they can. Let's see how.

WRITE QUICKLY

If you learn nothing else from this book than to write your article quickly, you will benefit more than you may ever realize. For if you write your article quickly it will have a strong style and a smoothness of ideas that will overcome any minor faults in grammar and composition.

So don't be overanxious about the mechanics of writing. If you must worry, then worry about the technical content of your article. Once you have your facts on paper, it is easy to revise.

Write quickly to keep your ideas flowing. If something new occurs to you while you are writing, include it. If the information is not pertinent you can easily delete it later. And if a sentence or paragraph does not seem to be as good as you think it should be, don't stop; keep writing. Make a short note in the margin and revise the material later.

Now let's summarize. Don't be overconcerned with punctuation, grammar, or the other mechanics of writing while you are putting words on paper. Instead, concentrate on getting a smooth flow of ideas. Write quickly and finish the article as soon as possible. If you do this your article will be stronger and there will be little chance of overlooking good ideas because you are too concerned with the mechanics of writing.

HOW TO POLISH

As soon as you finish your article, put it away and forget it for one week. Start to work on another article or some project which is not in any way related to the article you have finished. Don't review the finished article in your mind. Try to get as far away from the article as you possibly can.

After a week or so, at a time when your mind is clear and free of other problems, take the article out. Read it as though you had never seen it before. Read as quickly as you can. While you are reading, note in the margin any ideas that occur to you.

Try to be as critical as possible while you read the article. If a sentence or paragraph is not clear, mark it. If there is a sudden jump from one subject to another without a transition, mark it. Don't be afraid to be critical of your own work. Nothing but improvement can result.

If you find that a rewrite is necessary, don't hesitate—do it at once. If you put the rewrite off you will probably forget what was wrong. Remember that it is not shameful to rewrite—all good writers do.

FAULTS TO CHECK

Here are eight faults to check: (1) mile-long lead, (2) yard-long sentences, (3) big words, where shorter ones will do, (4) overly long paragraphs, (5) too many illustrations or tables, (6) unrelated material, (7) sloppy manuscript or illustrations, and (8) too much material for the length of article you plan. Any of these faults can mean the difference between acceptance and rejection of your article.

Mile-long leads. In your early writing attempts you may be so enthusiastic over your story that you try to tell it all in the lead—check your lead first. It should not be more than about five sentences. If it is longer, break the lead into two paragraphs.

Besides the physical length of your lead, you should also consider its idea content. Don't try to cram all the ideas of your article into the lead. If you do, you will give your reader an acute headache. Instead try to limit the idea content of your lead to the main idea of your article and possibly one or two other related ideas.

Yard-long sentences. When you write quickly you will use shorter sentences. But some of your ideas may be so complex that your sentences expand. So check for unusually long sentences.

There are few rules for ideal sentence length. In general the average length of sentences in your article should not exceed about twenty words. You can have much longer sentences if you need them, but be sure to follow a long sentence with a short one. And if you focus your attention on your reader's needs and interests, you will find that your sentences will be shorter than if you confine your effort to trying to impress your reader.

If you find many long sentences in your article, break them up. And while you are shortening your sentences try to eliminate useless words. You'll find that your sentences will become more accurate and the text of your article will move faster.

If you type your article yourself, watch for sentences that are longer than two typewritten lines. With one-inch margins the average typewritten line contains ten to twelve words. So a two-line sentence has 20 to 24 words. See to it that your article does not have many sentences longer than two typewritten lines.

Long words. Long words are usually abstract words. And as you learned in Chapter 7, abstract words can be poison to your readers. So be on guard for the big words. If you find three or four of them in one sentence ask yourself if they are necessary. Think about the big words—many are probably unnecessary. Get rid of them by using smaller, more familiar words.

Overly long paragraphs. A paragraph is like a milestone. Your reader feels a sense of accomplishment when he finishes a paragraph. But if you make your paragraphs too long your reader gets discouraged. He reads part of a paragraph, then skips to the next one.

For the modern technical article you should have about two paragraphs per typewritten page. There are few subjects today that rate a paragraph that runs a full typewritten page. Most long paragraphs can easily be broken into two or more paragraphs.

Review the excerpts of articles in Chapter 7. Note that most of these articles use short paragraphs. And where a long paragraph was necessary, most of the authors were careful to follow it with a short paragraph.

Too many illustrations or tables. Check a few modern business papers. You'll find that most of them use about two illustrations or tables per page. Some articles may have more and some less. But the average is two illustrations or tables per page.

So if you are planning to write a two-page article do not supply thirty illustrations. The editor cannot possibly use all these illustrations. Instead, choose the most important illustrations and supply these to the editor. If there is a choice of illustrations, supply the alternates but mark them properly. And note this fact in your letter to the editor.

Use as few tables as possible. Tables are expensive to set in type. And the average reader today does not expect a magazine to carry tables that properly belong in a catalog or handbook. Confine any table that you do use to a few important values. Your reader can still learn how to use the table. But he will be spared the glut of useless tabular material.

Unrelated material. If you are writing an article on piping, stick to pipes. Don't let your article wander. If you do, you will find that your article becomes weak. Since most engineers and scientists have special interests, they look for the narrow article that covers a particular area of their field. If your article wanders, you lose the many benefits that come from a concentrated discussion of a subject.

Sloppy manuscript or illustrations. Editors remember an author first for his technical skill and second for the condition of the manuscript he submits. Remember—the editor must work with your manuscript after he receives it. If your manuscript is in poor shape, the editor must spend extra time on it. And since all editors are busy people, you are imposing on their time when you submit a poorly prepared manuscript.

Have your manuscript typed by a professional. It may cost you a few dollars but the result will be worth it. And be sure that your illustrations are the best you can secure. Then the editor will be able to process your manuscript with the least effort.

Excess material. Try to gauge how much text and how many illustrations you need for the article. If you plan a two-page article you should have up to about six illustrations and about eight typewritten double-spaced pages. Again, note that all manuscripts or articles should be typed double-spaced. If you plan a longer article—say four published pages—the amount of typewritten material should be about double but you should have only six or eight illustrations.

OTHER FAULTS TO CHECK

Besides the faults listed above, check for the following. They are based on the recommendations of Robert Gunning, the well-known readability consultant.

1. Keep your sentences short.
2. Prefer the simple to the complex.
3. Use the familiar word.
4. Avoid unnecessary words.
5. Put action in your verbs.
6. Write as you talk.
7. Use pictureable terms.
8. Tie in with your reader's experience.
9. Make full use of variety (vary your style).
10. Write to express, not to impress.

The emphasis on readability in recent years makes it imperative that you learn and use these excellent rules. All editors today follow these or similar rules. So why take chances? Get your writing into tune with today's thinking. Learn all the techniques you can to improve your writing—then use them.

SUBMIT YOUR MANUSCRIPT

When your article is ready—after checking and topnotch preparation—send it to the editor. If you've talked with the editor about the article, you can deliver it by hand. But you don't gain much by this. No editor will reach his decision while you sit and wait. Editors demand privacy for this decision. And they deserve it!

So don't ask the editor to read your article while you sit in his office. It's embarrassing to him—and he's a busy man who reads from morning to night. Let him read the article when he has time— your chances of acceptance will be higher. You can just as easily mail your article, instead of delivering it by hand. If there's anything special you want the editor to know, write a short note of explanation. Keep a record of the date you sent in your article.

If your article contains photos and drawings, send it by registered mail. Use the replacement cost, or article payment you expect, whichever is greater, as the value for which you register the material.

Once your article is in the mail, don't immediately needle the editor for an acceptance. He may have received ten other articles the day yours arrived. Be patient. You'll hear from him in time. And if you don't hear from him you may see your article in print before it is even acknowledged. Some editors have peculiar work habits!

But if you don't hear from the editor in about three months, write him. He may have misplaced your article (this seldom happens), or his letter may have been lost in the mail. Don't scold him when you write. Just state that you mailed an article (give its title and number of illustrations) on a certain date, and politely ask him what has happened.

Once your article is accepted, don't hound the editor for a publication date. Scheduling a modern magazine is a tricky job. The editor may be forced to postpone your story at the last minute. And remember—editors work three months in advance. So an acceptance today means the soonest the article can appear is about three months hence.

Lastly—don't hound the editor for payment. He'll pay, if he said he would. But he, like all of us, has a budget. And if he went over it last month his payments this month may be delayed. Once again —be patient. Editors have long memories. They appreciate contributors who realize that editors are human too.

SUMMARY

Write quickly—polish at your leisure. But write—and polish. Don't neglect either. To polish an article, forget it for a while, then review it. Be as critical as you can while you reread it. From good criticism comes outstanding writing. Rewrite if you think it is necessary. Check for the various faults listed in this chapter. They will guide you to the most common mistakes. After you're satisfied your article is right, send it to the magazine you've chosen. Then be patient. Don't needle for acceptance, publication date, or payment.

CHAPTER CHECK-UP

1. What are the two troubles technical writers meet most frequently?
2. Give the steps you should follow in polishing an article.
3. Name eight faults to check for. Discuss each.
4. What ten readability recommendations should you keep in mind?
5. How should you submit your manuscript?
6. What interval is considered reasonable before asking an editor about your article?
7. Why should you never needle an editor about acceptance, publication, or payment?

Chapter 10

HOW TO WRITE TECHNICAL PAPERS

As an engineer, scientist, or technical writer, sooner or later you'll be asked to write a technical paper. The request may come from an engineering or scientific society, a government agency, or some similar group. But regardless of the source of the request, try to accept it. You'll profit in many ways. For technical papers are different from articles and require that you use a different approach. Let's see how papers differ from technical articles.

HOW TECHNICAL PAPERS AND ARTICLES DIFFER

Your technical paper may differ from an article in six ways: (1) subject matter, (2) approach to subject, (3) length, (4) type of mathematics used, (5) depth of coverage, and (6) the message for its readers.

Subject matter. Technical papers often cover an extremely limited phase of a subject. For example, you could write a paper on The Effect of Fillet Radii on Bolt Strength. Or you might write a paper on The Operating Experience with Dual-circulation Boilers Using 72 Per Cent Make-up. Other subjects for technical papers might be Stack Heights to Minimize Ground Concentrations, and Production and Installation of Vertical Waterwheel Generators.

Note the main characteristics of these subjects—detailed treatment of a specific problem. Most of these subjects are too narrow for the usual business-magazine article. Many technical papers take a comprehensive look at a single problem. Most modern business-magazine articles take a broader look at a large problem, or several problems. In choosing an idea for a technical paper you need not be concerned with the number of readers who may have the same problem. As long as there is one reader having the same or a similar problem, writing and publication of your paper can be justified.

Of course technical papers can cover a wide area too. But even here you'll find a difference between papers and articles. In writing a technical paper to cover a broad area you'd make every effort to include all the references you can find. In an article on the same subject you'd probably limit yourself to the most important references.

Approach to the subject. Many technical papers try to examine every phase of a problem. Business-magazine articles shun minute details, confine their attention to the major factors. The reader of your technical paper is often most interested in a complete statement of the problem, its background, and all the possible solutions. Business-magazine readers usually look for a quick, direct solution to a problem. So you must approach the subject of your paper differently from that of your article.

Length. Your technical paper will often be longer than your article on the same subject. Why? Because the paper considers more phases of the subject. While some societies limit the number of words you can use in a paper, others place no limit at all on paper length.

In modern business magazines the length of a published article seldom exceeds 12 pages. This immediately limits the length of your text and the number of illustrations you can use. In writing an article you must be more selective than in a paper. If you aren't the editor will be.

Mathematics. Articles use applied mathematics to solve the problems discussed. Derivations of mathematical concepts are hardly ever used. But in a paper you can derive every relation if necessary.

Few business magazines today publish articles using advanced math —like calculus or differential equations. But in your technical paper you can use calculus or any other branch of higher math. Technical societies hardly ever limit the math you use.

Depth of coverage. Technical papers can trace a subject from its beginnings centuries ago to its present state. But in an article you must generally limit your coverage to modern applications. Your paper can examine every phase of a subject, regardless of how many words, illustrations, or tables are needed. In an article you must confine your treatment to those items that are immediately useful to your readers.

Your message. Many articles written today urge the reader to adopt a certain technique, investigate his present way of doing things, or change his concepts. There is an immediacy about an article—you deal with active problems. Many papers do not urge any action by their readers. Instead the paper reports past and present thinking.

You can think of papers as reporting facts without "sell." In a technical paper you might report experiments and studies of flow through an orifice of a certain diameter. The conclusions you draw may in no way influence your reader to change his thinking about the orifice. They may just expand his knowledge of this particular orifice.

Of course, not every article "sells" its readers. Some articles simply report present events and technology. But articles more often than technical papers try to help the reader solve his problems in new or different ways. Articles that do this may be said to have some "sell" in them.

TECHNICAL PAPERS ARE IMPORTANT

Technical papers serve an important function in modern technology. They give the complete coverage many engineers and scientists need. And more and more engineers and scientists are writing papers today than ever before. Our technology is advancing so rapidly that only by studying the experience of others can we move beyond the limits of our own work.

The technical paper has a permanent place in the archives of the organization sponsoring it. Here your paper serves as raw material for future researchers in the field. And since the quality of a technical paper must be the highest, these archives are regarded as prime research sources by all engineers and scientists.

With more engineers and scientists writing papers today you must strive harder to make your material good. The American Society of Mechanical Engineers published 553 technical papers in 1953 and 859 in 1957. This is a rise of about 60 per cent. So if you seek to publish a paper—and you should if you have suitable material—you must be ready to develop the skills that are needed. An outstanding technical paper helps you understand your work better, stands as a permanent record of your activities, contributes to your professional standing, and widens your acquaintanceship with the other workers in your chosen field. Let's see how you can prepare your papers better, and with less waste of time and energy.

HOW TECHNICAL PAPERS ARE DEVELOPED

There are two ways in which technical papers are developed: (1) A division or committee of a society or other organization requests an author to prepare a paper on a certain subject. (2) The author writes a paper and submits it, unsolicited, to an engineering or scientific society.

Solicited papers. Here the society, through one of its divisions or committees, chooses you to write a paper, usually covering a phase of your work. And the more specialized your work, the greater the chance of your being asked to prepare a paper.

It is well not to turn down such requests. For you'll find that most societies will give up after you've turned down three or more invitations to write a paper. And since a solicited paper has a better chance of acceptance, you're losing a good opportunity.

When the society contacts you about doing a paper on a certain subject, take some time to think it over. Don't agree to write the paper unless you know the subject well. If you're more familiar with another phase of the subject, tell the society. Most committee members (these are the people who actually make the request to you in the name of the society) think about the subject in general terms. So don't be embarrassed when asking to have the subject revised. You're the one who must write and present the paper.

Remember that your paper will be read by many of your co-workers in the field. So be sure that you choose the appropriate phase of your subject. Otherwise you may find that your paper is not as well received as it should be.

Unsolicited papers. Here you choose your subject without the aid of the society. And since your paper has not been solicited, it may conflict with one the society has already requested from another author. Naturally, the society will give preference to a paper it solicits.

It's a good idea to write an unsolicited paper every few years. Even if it isn't accepted, the society becomes aware of you and your interest in writing technical papers. You may find that the society will solicit a paper from you a year or so after your unsolicited paper was turned down. But the exact procedure varies considerably from one society to another.

Use the hints given at the beginning of this chapter when you choose a subject for a paper. Probably the best source of ideas for technical papers is your everyday work. If this is at all unusual or highly specialized, a technical paper on some phase of the work is probably justified.

Contact members of the society before choosing the final subject for your paper. Many members have strong ideas on good subjects for papers. If you choose one of these subjects, or a variation of one, your unsolicited paper has a better chance of acceptance.

You need not be a member of a society to write a paper for it. But most societies are more sympathetic to papers submitted by members than by nonmembers. You should, of course, be a member of the society representing your profession. But you need not be a member of related societies unless such membership offers advantages.

HOW PAPERS ARE PROCESSED

All large technical societies follow a specific routine in handling papers. Figure 10-1 shows the procedure used by The American Society of Mechanical Engineers. While other societies may use slightly different procedures, there is a general similarity. Understanding what ASME does will help you to understand your own society better. Their procedure is as follows:

Origin. The paper is either solicited or contributed, as shown at the top of Fig. 10-1. In either case you inform the editorial department of the society of your intention to submit the paper. With a solicited paper, write the editorial department, informing them of the title of your paper, its approximate length, and when you expect to submit it. If you wish to present the paper at a certain meeting of the society, ask the editorial department if your proposed delivery date allows enough time for review and preprinting.

An unsolicited paper can be submitted directly to the editorial department with a covering letter. Explain why you wrote the paper, when and at what meeting you'd like to present it, and what segment of the society membership it will interest.

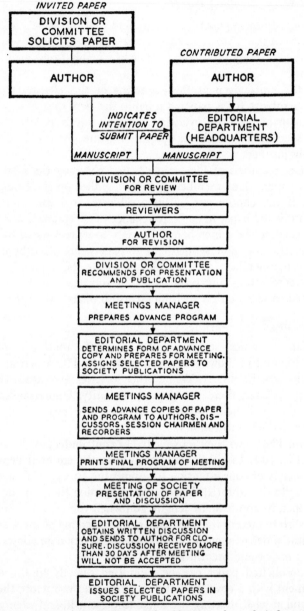

Fig. 10-1. Steps in the submission to and publication of a technical paper by the American Society of Mechanical Engineers.

136

Review. No matter what the origin of your paper, it will be reviewed by technical specialists in your field. They will review it for technical content and writing clarity and check for commercial bias. Your paper will be returned for revision if the reviewers find this necessary. Revise your paper according to their recommendations. Unless you do, there is little chance of the paper being accepted for publication.

Publication. Once your paper is revised and has been accepted the editorial department begins its job. In almost every society today your paper is preprinted before the meeting at which you present it. Preprints may be mimeographed or set in type, depending on the practice of the society. And the paper may be selected for publication in one of the society's journals.

Meeting arrangements. While your paper is being published, arrangements for the meeting are being made. Figure 10-1 shows the steps. Be sure to cooperate fully with the society during these arrangements. You can make the job of the meetings manager much easier if you submit all your copy on time, fill out the required forms correctly, and follow the society recommendations on the preparation of text, illustrations, and tables.

Discussion. Your paper will probably evoke both written and oral discussion from your audience. Be prepared to answer your discussors. If they ask for information you don't have when you present your paper, prepare an answer immediately after you leave the meeting room. For the sooner you do this important part of presenting a paper, the easier it will be.

WRITING THE TECHNICAL PAPER

The steps in writing a technical paper are the same as in writing an article. Briefly, you should (1) prepare an outline, (2) gather data, (3) choose your illustrations, (4) write the rough draft, (5) polish the rough draft, (6) check all your facts, and (7) submit the paper to the society. Let's take a quick look at the various elements of a technical paper to see how you can best handle them. Many of the following suggestions are based on data published by the leading engineering societies—ASME, AIEE, ASCE, and AIME.

Style. Technical papers tend to be more formal than business-magazine articles. But this is not a valid reason for writing in a verbose and pedantic way.

The chief purpose of your paper is to convey information to your readers. Use simple terms and expressions. If you must introduce new words or concepts, define them immediately after you use them the first time. Keep your sentences, thoughts, and definitions concise. Write for the average engineer or scientist—not for the specialist.

Avoid personal bias when using the first person or referring to individuals by name. Use product names only in your acknowledgments, if possible.

Spelling and usage. Use Webster's New International Dictionary as a guide to spelling and preferred usage. Check the spelling of all technical terms and names before submitting your paper.

Length of the paper. Some societies specify the minimum and maximum lengths allowed for their papers. For example, ASME suggests that the text not exceed 4,000 words (about fourteen pages of double-spaced typescript). Avoid long quotations. Instead, refer to the source of the quotation.

Use illustrations and tables where they help clarify your text and where they demonstrate results. Omit detailed drawings, lengthy test data and calculations, and photos which, though interesting, are not necessarily important to the understanding of the subject. Manuscripts that do not meet the requirements of the society are usually returned for revision and condensation. When you don't think you can treat your subject adequately within the limits set by the society, check with the sponsoring division or committee. You may be able to obtain permission to present a longer paper.

Approvals and clearances. As with articles, it is your responsibility to secure all company approvals necessary. And never overlook government clearance on classified material. When you have obtained any needed approvals or clearances, in writing, make a note on your manuscript that these have been secured. Keep the approvals or clearances in your file.

Contents of the paper. The desired order of contents for the usual technical paper is (*a*) title, (*b*) author's name, title, business firm, and mailing address, (*c*) abstract, (*d*) body of paper, (*e*) appendixes, (*f*) acknowledgments, (*g*) bibliography, (*h*) tables, (*i*) captions for illustrations, (*j*) illustrations, including photos, charts, diagrams, and sketches. Insert short tables up to eight lines in the text, immediately after their first mention. Put longer tables at the end of the text.

With your paper prepared in this order the editorial department of the society can, if necessary, rearrange the illustrations. Some societies have recently switched to a two-column format for papers. Illustrations are located as near their first text reference as possible. This reduces the amount of page-flipping the reader must do.

Title. Make the title of your paper explicit, descriptive, and as short as possible. Use an explanatory subtitle to clarify the meaning of the main title if this seems necessary.

Author's name. The name of the author (or authors) should appear immediately below the title of the paper, at the top of the first page. Insert the author's title and business connection as a footnote in the lower left-hand corner of the first page.

Abstract. Write a short abstract (50 to 100 words) of your paper. Have it typed on the first page of the paper, immediately ahead of the first paragraph of your paper. Do not try to condense the entire substance of your paper into the abstract. Instead, give a clear statement of its object and scope, and the results achieved. Then your reader can quickly decide if the entire text of the paper will interest him. Here are two typical abstracts:

Electrodynamic apparatus is described for producing and identifying torsional resonances in a small cast iron sample. Shear modulus is computed from the resonant frequencies. A specimen is taken from the mold of each crankshaft. Accuracy of the procedure is discussed. More than 1000 tests have been made and the relation of shear modulus to other measurable physical properties is demonstrated.[1]

Several special relations are derived that may be used to simplify the solution of certain phases of the torsional vibration problem. A solution is described for the vibration of a system with an untuned viscous damper.

Numerical values are given for the non-linear elasticity of the Falk-Bibby type couplings. These values are re-arranged into a form suitable for calculating undamped resonance curves of an engine installation which includes one of these couplings. An approximate solution for the resulting vibration is described and illustrated by calculation.[2]

[1] From J. D. Swannack and R. J. Maddock, A Dynamic Shear Modulus Apparatus and Production Test Results for a Cast Crankshaft Alloy, ASME paper.

[2] From F. P. Porter, Torsional Vibration Notes with Solutions for An Untuned Viscous Damper and a Flexible Coupling with Non-Linear Elasticity, ASME paper.

Body of the paper. Organize the text of the body of your paper as you would for an article. Start with initial facts and proceed through your story to your conclusions. Or use a time sequence, starting with the earliest date of importance and proceeding to the present.

State your purpose or aim at the start. Then your reader will have a clear concept of the objective as he proceeds. Follow the aim or purpose with a description of the problem, the means used to solve it, and other related information important to the results and conclusions. Lastly, present the results. Follow these with your conclusions.

Appendixes. If your paper is highly mathematical, develop equations and formulas in an appendix rather than the body of your paper. This makes reading easier. You can also use appendixes for detailed descriptions of apparatus and other related material not essential to the general presentation of your subject.

Acknowledgments. Insert these at the end of the text, before your bibliography.

Bibliographies and References. Refer to literature cited as follows: (1) If you have only four or five references, use footnotes in the text. (2) If you have more than five references, use a bibliography at the end of your paper. Number references serially. In the text the numbers for these references should appear in parentheses. With the first reference, use the following footnote: Numbers in parentheses refer to similarly numbered references in bibliography at end of paper.

Arrange your references like this: (a) For a book, give author (with his initials), title of book, publisher, city, number of edition, year of publication, and page numbers. (b) For a periodical, give title of article, author (with his initials), name of periodical (not abbreviated), volume, number, year, page numbers.

Use extreme care when preparing your references. A single error in volume number, year, or page number can waste much time. Keep in mind the reader who may order photostatic copies of an article or book page by mail; picture his annoyance if the reference is wrong.

Tables. Type tables of six to eight lines as part of the text. But locate the table so that it does not run over onto a second page. Type larger tables on *separate* sheets and put them at the end of the text. Give each table a suitable descriptive heading. Number the tables consecutively and refer to them in the text by number. Do not use references like "the following table" or "the table on page 3." Identify each table with the author's name.

Captions. Type your captions for illustrations double-spaced. Put them on a separate sheet of paper. Identify each caption by using the figure number ahead of it. Type your name at the top of each sheet of captions.

Photographs. Submit only clear, sharp glossy prints. Do not mount or paste the photos to the manuscript. Instead, gather all photos and drawings and place them between stiff cardboard at the end of the text. Lightly mark the figure number and your name on the back of each photo. Use a grease pencil so the face of the print is not marred. Do not use paper clips on photos.

Other Illustrations. Use black ink and heavy white paper or tracing cloth for graphs, charts, line drawings, and sketches. Blueprints, photostats, and black-line prints are unsuitable. Mark the figure number and your name on the back of each drawing. Never paste your illustrations to the text pages. And do not draw on the text pages.

Society responsibility. Remember—you, and not the society, are responsible for any statement or opinion in your paper, discussion, or other published material. So check your text, illustrations, and tables carefully. Be sure your math is correct. Make certain that all Greek letters which may be confused with English letters (alpha, omega, rho, nu, etc.) are clearly marked.

Manuscript due dates. Many societies require that you submit the manuscript of your paper at least four months in advance of the meeting at which it will be presented. This much time is needed for review, revision, recommendation for presentation and publication, editing, typesetting, printing, and distribution to prospective discussors. Never flirt with this deadline. Submit your manuscript on time. Otherwise you may find your paper overlooked.

Discussors. When submitting your manuscript, include a list of persons you'd like to invite to discuss your paper. Then the society will send advance copies of your paper to these people. This permits the invited people to prepare either written or oral remarks.

Publication by others. Many societies urge their authors to seek the widest possible audience for their papers. They encourage publication of a paper by others once it has been presented at a society meeting or published by the society. So you may find that the paper you visualized as suitable only for society use being widely published outside the society. Check with the society to learn the exact procedure to follow.

Authors' expenses. The dues paid to a society by its members do not provide sufficient funds to pay the expenses you incur in preparing a paper and attending a meeting to present the paper. You, or your company, must pay all these expenses. Technical societies hardly ever pay an honorarium for papers they publish.

SUMMARY

Technical papers differ from articles in a number of ways. The usual paper covers a narrower field; many are highly mathematical. Most papers are longer than the usual business-magazine article. Since papers have a permanent place in the archives of the society sponsoring them, writing a technical paper is an important task. Papers may be either solicited or unsolicited. Every society follows its own established procedure when processing a paper. Follow the directions of the society sponsoring your paper. Use the same basic procedures in writing a technical paper as you do in writing an article.

CHAPTER CHECK-UP

1. What types of organizations are likely to ask you to prepare a technical paper?
2. What should you do when asked to prepare a paper? Why?
3. List six ways in which technical papers differ from articles. Discuss each of these differences.
4. How does the message in a paper differ from that in an article? Why does this difference occur?
5. Why are technical papers important?
6. Describe the two ways in which papers originate. In each case what precautions should you take?
7. Can you change the subject of a solicited paper? Why? How should you make this change?
8. Describe the manner in which a typical technical paper is processed by the society sponsoring it.
9. What are seven steps you should take when preparing a technical paper?
10. List the preferred contents of a typical technical paper.

11. Prepare an abstract for a typical technical paper. What should this abstract contain?
12. Describe how you would prepare an appendix for a technical paper. What should it include?
13. Describe how you would prepare a bibliography for a technical paper. When do you use a bibliography instead of footnotes?
14. How are discussors obtained for technical papers? How can you help the society find suitable discussors for your paper?

Chapter 11

WRITING REPORTS THAT GET ACTION

You can write reports that get results. But you'll need more than a well-oiled typewriter, a sharpened pencil, or a topnotch secretary. You'll need showmanship, imagination, and a satchelful of planning. For reports often involve more personal selling of your writing than do articles or technical papers.

WHY WRITE A REPORT?

You write a report instead of a memo, article, or letter when you want to do more than just record information. You write a report to get action. It may be action on any kind of proposal—on that proposal for a new preventive maintenance program, on your request for new materials-handling equipment, on your recommendation for a change in the layout of your department. It may be the nod to go ahead on a new storage building or the money to replace outmoded machine tools with high-speed models. Then, of course, there is the long-familiar report of extended tests, new products, plant location, or various alternatives in a certain proposal.

To get the action you desire you must (1) decide in advance what you want the report to do for you, (2) determine how to write your report so that it gets to the top man for approval, (3) phrase the report so that you will get the approval you want.

KINDS OF REPORTS

There are hundreds of reports used in industry and business today. Many popular types you'll meet are routine in nature. They deal with

144

weekly, monthly, or annual production, stock, earnings, etc. We'll overlook these in this book because the form, length, and other details are often standardized. Also, there's relatively little originality needed to prepare routine reports. Two other common types of industrial reports are the *short-form* and the *long-form.*

Short-form reports are usually thought of as being six pages or less in length. Many of these are routine. The nonroutine short-form report may be: (1) a letter or memo, or (2) a condensed version of the long-form report. Some writing authorities define a long-form report as having more than six pages—others say more than ten pages. In this book we'll define a long-form report as one having more than about six double-spaced typed pages and following the outline given later in this chapter.

When writing a short-form report as a letter or memo, follow the outline given in this chapter for a long-form report, but delete sections and headings, as necessary. By following the outline given in this chapter you will preserve a certain logical structure for your letter or memo. As such, it's sure to be more effective.

To condense the long-form outline, simply write less for each topic. And delete those topics that do not apply. Once again, you'll be casting your report in a long-recognized form. Your reader will find the report easier to read and use.

So use the instructions in this chapter for all except routine reports. You'll find the instructions are particularly useful for the long-form report so popular in research, manufacturing, sales, and other functions.

IDEAS MUST BE SOLD

Being in command of good ideas for improvement or of important data from tests is only half your battle. You have to make their "profit potential" clear to top management. Your findings and conclusions must be precise and clear. This is where some engineers and scientists fall down. After all, you are urging others to spend money and effort on *your* ideas. So to get approval you must show how your ideas will pay off in profit of some kind.

Your report may have to run the whole course of supervisors right up through the board of directors. For success, it must not be stopped at any point along the line.

Ideally a report should be written a little differently for each man as it passes up the line. As Fig. 11-1 shows, the training, interests, and thinking of executives change substantially as your report moves upward. At the scientific levels, technicians, engineers, and production managers are more likely to give the greatest weight to engineering feasibility. At the upper end of the organization, the president and the board of directors will be much more concerned with the financial feasibility of the project and its prospects for profit.

IF YOUR REPORT
GOES TO THESE MEN.... WATCH THE SHIFT OF INTEREST

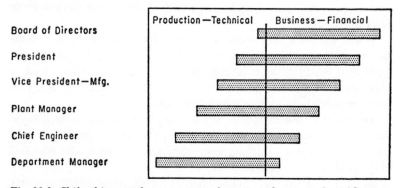

Fig. 11-1. Shift of interest from one type of report reader to another. (*Courtesy of Factory Management and Maintenance*)

FIVE ESSENTIALS OF GOOD REPORTS

The surest way to appeal to both the technical and the financial interests of your supervisors—and to make certain these extremely busy men read at least the vital elements of your report—is to do the following five things:

Start with your summary. Put your best foot forward by briefly stating the heart of your proposal or findings in the first paragraph of the report. Call this section *Summary, Conclusions,* or *Recommendations.* Answer quickly the all-important questions: Will it work? What will this do for our company? and How much will it cost?

A good sentence to get into the first paragraph of your report is "This project will substantially increase the company profits because. . . ." If you can't make such a claim, or can't state positive findings, there's little chance of getting anyone to read further or to give approval. Try to show your reader, in summary form, how advantages minus costs equals net gains.

Use a table of contents. This gives your reader a chance to select what he wants to read. He can also tell from the contents how you've organized your report and what kind of emphasis you've given various elements.

Put detailed technical and statistical data in an appendix. This shortens and speeds the presentation of your main ideas and the persuasive parts of the report. Yet it makes tables, charts, diagrams, and other substantiating data available to those who must pass on the accuracy and objectivity of your report.

Provide an index. You help your reader find specific items when you provide an index. The index also saves time. Use the index for all long reports; omit it from most short reports, unless you feel it would help the reader.

Follow a standard report form. Many firms have a standard report form. Follow it exactly. Your supervisors will hardly put any thought into your report if you can't follow company rules. If your firm doesn't have a standard form, use the form given below.

MAKE IT EASY TO SAY YES

Building the report to get it read is one thing. It's just as important to design it for an answer that says *Approved.* How do you do this?

Think through every problem that's likely to arise in carrying out your proposal. Then provide an acceptable answer to show you've anticipated and planned for every such circumstance. A busy executive has all sorts of issues to settle—and plenty of worries of his own. If he must stop and solve a problem before he can approve your proposal, the easiest and quickest thing for him to do is to say no.

So check your report plans. Do they answer your reader's major questions?

What is the subject?
Why should *I* be interested?
What is the story in a nutshell?
What action is recommended?
Why?

Developing the answers to these questions will provide the material for your report.

HOW TO WRITE YOUR REPORT

Once you've decided where and how you're going to aim your report, you must consider the fundamentals of its construction. Remember—the usual report differs from a technical article. Reports are more detailed and comprehensive. Many reports are written for a narrow, highly specialized audience. In an article you have a more general readership. Reports usually follow a known pattern—articles vary, depending on their subject matter.

Reports resemble the technical paper, in some respects. Many technical papers start as reports. The material is converted to paper form by the author before presentation. So the report-writing hints in this chapter can be used with the technical paper hints in Chapter 10.

ORGANIZING THE LONG-FORM REPORT

Good organization of your report is a must. In itself it demonstrates clear and orderly thinking.

Try using 3- by 5-in. file cards for organizing your facts and ideas. Write each major fact or idea on a separate card. Spread them all out on a table top. Then spend half an hour or so regrouping them into the best sequence for developing your ideas.

Check the sequence against the following typical arrangement of long-form report sections. This arrangement is widely used throughout industry, schools, and colleges for all kinds of formal reports.

1. *Report title.* Choose your report title with care. Make it descriptive, accurate, interesting, brief.

2. *Title page.* Center title on the page. Leave generous margins. Include the name of the recipient, preceded by "Submitted to," or some similar designation. Place your name below this, and the date at the bottom of the page. If the report has an identifying number or letter, place it at the bottom of the page, just above the date.

3. *Summary, conclusions, or recommendations.* Reduce these to essentials. Tell what you propose, why it will be worthwhile when accepted, and what it will cost. Make the purpose of your report clear. Give the major conclusions exactly. Call attention to your detailed

recommendations (which may be stated in great length in the body or appendix) for carrying out the purpose of the report.

4. *Table of contents.* List the headings exactly as worded in the report. Prepare the table of contents from your 3 by 5 cards, after you've grouped them in the desired sequence. Give inclusive page numbers so your reader can tell how long each section of the report is.

5. *Preface or introduction.* Use where you think a brief definition of the problem and approach will clarify your conclusions. Put it on a separate page and keep it brief. Since the preface gives the reader his first contact with the subject, be sure you (*a*) state the subject of the report, (*b*) tell why the report was written, and (*c*) tell how you treat the subject in the report. In your preface you get together with the reader and give him a short review of what follows. You will also raise a number of questions in his mind.

6. *Body of the report.* This is where you define the problem in de-tail, state your approach, develop your logic, and support your arguments and conclusions. Include details of the equipment used (if any), procedure you followed, results obtained, and your recommendations, based on the conclusions you drew. Support your findings with important charts, graphs, diagrams, and tables. But save for the appendix the detailed illustrations used to develop your conclusions.

7. *Terminal section.* Here you answer the questions raised in the preface or introduction. None of the questions in the introduction should be omitted from the terminal section. Your treatment of this section is extremely important. Properly handled, the terminal section reinforces the conclusions drawn or recommendations made in the body of the report.

Your terminal section can be (*a*) factual—giving a simplified, comprehensive summary for your reader to retain; (*b*) critical—telling what you found wrong with the subject; (*c*) advisory—ranging from mild suggestions to definite recommendations.

Give your terminal section a definite heading like "Recommendations," "Results," "Limits of Application," "Some Common Uses," "Some Probable Developments," "Pertinent Suggestions," "Work in Prospect," "Merits of the Plan," "Some Important Correlations," or "Important Precautions." You can omit the terminal section if there appears to be no need for it.

8. *Bibliography.* List your reference sources here, if you think they would help the reader. But be specific. If you referred to only one chapter of a book in doing your research, cite only that one chapter and give the page numbers.

9. *Credits.* It pays to be generous in giving other people credit. But don't stretch this beyond the point of reasonableness. In the credits section you have a chance to win people to your side—the people and organizations who helped you develop your report. Their approval and cooperation may be very important to you and your project in the future.

10. *Appendixes.* Here is where you should put the mass of technical data, development and proof of formulas, details of comparative exhibits, charts, and diagrams. This is the reading gallery for the technical man, not the top manager.

11. *Index.* Use an index for long, formal reports. Omit it from short, routine reports. Prepare the index carefully—it will be a big help to your readers, and to yourself at a later date when you try to find some item whose location slips your mind.

WRITING STYLE

When choosing your phrasing and vocabulary, don't try to show off, especially with technical terms and unrelated philosophical concepts. Big words and long sentences never impress people.

Your writing should be clear and easily understood—even by the least technical reader. Writing that isn't clear makes a "no" answer more likely. Top management won't put money or time into your ideas unless they feel they completely understand everything you're talking about. Obscure language may be taken as a cover-up for a joker in the deck, or for some avenue of investigation that has been overlooked.

And give your spelling a special check. There's no point in having misspelled words mar your effort.

To speed up reading use (1) index tabs, and (2) footnotes to your text. Index tabs make it easy for the reader to refer from one section to another. Footnotes rid you of slowing down the nontechnical reader in the middle of your text by going into detail to explain an assumption you've made. Better include this material as a footnote at the bottom of the page. Then it'll be physically separate from the text. What might have become a difficult hurdle in your text then becomes optional reading.

MAKE YOUR REPORT INVITING

Solid pages of text are deadly. They're monotonous, discouraging, make the reader feel he must concentrate too much. To open up your pages, try these simple methods:

Break up the text. Indicate section heads, for instance, in solid capital letters. Indent subheads—or set flush left. Type them in caps-and-lower-case, underline them. Set off important paragraphs by underlining or by letting them stand alone in a block.

Use photos. They've got power. Use them wherever they will do a better, faster job of telling your story. Search manufacturer's catalogs, check with your public relations man or purchasing agent if you want to illustrate a product. Attach magazine articles about successful applications of your recommendations to similar problems in other companies.

Include charts and graphs. If you have to present numerical data, a graph summarizes quicker than a table. See Chapter 8.

Get attention with color. Use it wherever you want to highlight an important factor. Colored gummed stars and index tabs will help attract attention. Try putting your report in a colored folder. Choose a cheerful, optimistic shade—such as a light pastel. Or type your recommendation page on a colored sheet. But be careful to keep the colors in good taste.

DRAMATIZE YOUR REPORT

Reports can get action from top management—and can make research ideas pay off. Here's an example of one that did at International Business Machines. It got the green signal from IBM's management. And management gave its author a budget, relieved him of other work, put him in charge—the first project of his own—and promoted him.

This was the idea: The author believed there were market possibilities for special binoculars making use of infrared rays for seeing through fog. Besides writing a provocative report to top management, he added exhibit material that made it an eye-catcher. Here's a sampling of the exhibits that supported the proposal.

To emphasize loss of life and property damage during heavy fog:

1. Illustrated newspaper article headline, "Night Boat and Freighter Collide in River Fog."

2. Another article with headline, "Liners Crash in Fog."

3. News photos of vessel grounded because of fog.

To emphasize losses of aircraft in fog:

4. Letter from U.S. Department of Commerce, Aeronautics Branch, answering inquiry for figures, plus Bulletin titled "Civil Aircraft Accidents and Casualties."

To support the scientific aspects of his proposal:

5. Sheet from *Electronics* magazine, showing how infrared rays are related to visible rays, radio, x-rays, etc.

6. Article from *Science Supplement* stating that a photocell can "see" lights through fog.

7. Photostat of article stating that city of Washington had been photographed from airplane through fog, using infrared rays.

And so on, to a total of 20 exhibits, building the story of the profit potential of the project, and the means of accomplishing it.

HOW TO DELIVER YOUR REPORT

Even the best of reports have trouble flying alone. That's why it's smart to get yours off the ground with a personal boost.

Start with your own supervisor. He has to be sold on your proposal before he'll pass it up the line. It's a good idea to wait until he's in a receptive mood. Be sure to avoid springing your report on him when he's distracted by important problems or when he's just been on the receiving end of bad news.

When you've picked the right opportunity, deliver your report in person. Don't trust it to the office mails or surrender it to his secretary. Instead, make an appointment with him. Tell him you'd like to see him briefly at his convenience. If it's a special job you've done on your own initiative, assure him it hasn't distracted you from your regular assignments.

Suggest you'd be glad to sit quietly by while he reads the summary of your report. Perhaps he may want to ask some questions to clarify it. If, as is more probable, he says he'll read it and discuss it with you later, then tactfully suggest a definite date.

If your supervisor likes the report and sends it up through channels, you can expect to be called into a committee or conference to answer questions about it. Here's where all your planning and research will pay off. You'll have a chance to defend your reasoning, provide additional details, and do a personal selling job.

HOW TO RESEARCH YOUR REPORT

Good reports are based on sound facts, a wide knowledge of alternate solutions to problems, creative imagination, and intelligent selection of the most promising elements. You know the expression "A man's judgment is no better than his information." If you want your information to be sound, don't sit down and write a report or proposal without doing some research. Besides getting all the help you can from authorities, suppliers, and your own investigation in the plant, it's a good idea to tap other sources. Here's a list of some of the best sources in the United States for written information:

Technical journals in the field concerned. Consult the *Standard Rate and Data* at your library. If you need further information, write the editors of the magazines in your field.

Technical societies. Ask for directories of engineering and technical societies in your public or scientific library. Then write to the societies' headquarters, addressing your letters to the executive secretary.

Trade associations. See their publications, and the *Directory of National Trade Associations,* available from the U.S. Government Printing Office (see below for address). Write the executive secretary of the appropriate association.

Books. The *U.S. Catalog* lists all books in print in English in 1928. Books published since 1928 are in the *Cumulative Book Index.* Issued monthly; combined quarterly and yearly. Also includes a list of publishers, with addresses.

Indexes of Technical Magazines. See the *Industrial Arts Index,* issued monthly and yearly. Very useful. Also see the *Engineering Index, Chemical Abstracts, Science Abstracts, Electronics Abstracts, Agricultural Index, Biological Abstracts, Quarterly Cumulative Index Medicus,* etc. Many of these contain summaries from which you can obtain enough information to decide if reading the original is necessary.

Other indexes. Three popular ones are: *Readers Guide to Periodical*

Literature, issued monthly and yearly; *Vertical File Index,* issued in pamphlet form; *New York Times Index,* which covers newspaper-reported items. Rag-paper (permanent) edition of *The New York Times* is available in leading libraries.

Indexes of patents. Large libraries have bound volumes of the patents issued each year, arranged by numbers, called the *Annual Index of Inventors.* The Search Room in the U.S. Patent Office in Washington, D.C., is the only place where patents are available and organized by subject. You can use the room, if you wish.

Public libraries. Ask the librarians—they can be a big help. Also see the general catalog of the library.

Special Libraries Association. Ask your librarian about this association.

Authors of articles, books. Write them, if you think they can help you. Be sure to address them care of their *publishers,* not their job or university connection. (Men change jobs faster than they do publishers).

Famous men. If you have need for their help, write them questions. The cooperation and answers will be a surprise and help to you. For addresses, ask local newspapers, librarians. Also, see *Who's Who.*

Directories. Check these: *Moody's Industrials, Thomas' Register of American Manufacturers, city directories.*

Government publications. Write the Superintendent of Documents, Government Printing Office, Washington 25, D.C. Ask for titles and prices of publications in your field. Many are nominally priced; some are free.

REMINDER FOR REPORT WRITING

Here is a tried and proved four-step scheme to follow when you write any kind of formal report. Use it and you won't overlook any important parts of your report.

STEP 1: PREPARE YOUR MATERIAL

    1. Collect information, facts, illustrations
    2. Check to see you have all detailed information needed
    3. Decide on the purpose of your report
        Who will read it?
        Why does he want it?

What does he require?

How will he use it?

4. Draft a key sentence, stating your main objectives for the report

STEP 2: PLAN YOUR REPORT

1. Classify your material, using topic cards described earlier
2. Make an outline
3. Make a complete list of major and minor subject headings

STEP 3: WRITE YOUR REPORT

1. Introduction: state subject, purpose, plan; summarize results, conclusions
2. Body: describe equipment, procedures, results
3. Terminal section: summarize findings; make recommendations; give final emphasis
4. Abstract or synopsis: condense report in paragraph or two (if needed)
5. Prepare table of contents
6. Assemble and organize appendix and bibliography

STEP 4: CRITICIZE YOUR REPORT

1. Examine report as a whole; the plan; the proportioning of parts
2. Check agreement of title, table of contents, introduction and abstract or synopsis
3. Check agreement of terminal section and the introduction
4. Check agreement of headings with table of contents
5. Check proportion of paragraphs, sentences
6. Examine details of text transitions from topic to topic, part to part, sentence structure, wording

LETTER OF TRANSMITTAL

Some firms require special letters of transmittal for all reports. If your firm is one of these, follow the requirements exactly. Never allow the report to leave your hands before you've checked the letter of transmittal. Mistakes in this letter can be fatal to your report.

If your firm has no special requirements for a transmittal letter, give the matter some serious thought. Your letter accompanying the report should contain the name of the person to whom the report is addressed and state why the report was written, who authorized your writing of it, and the date when the report was requested.

Keep the letter as short as possible—two paragraphs should be all you need for the average report. Since the letter of transmittal acts as a record of the delivery of the report, keep all other details out of it.

If you try to summarize the report in the transmittal letter, the man receiving the report will never go further than the letter. So all the effort you put into your report will be wasted.

Sign the transmittal letter, *in ink*. Then be sure the letter and report reach the person to whom they are addressed. In many formal reports the letter of transmittal is bound in the report. It precedes the title page of the report.

SUMMARY

Reports can get action, if they are correctly planned and well-written. Good reports are written in such a manner that it is almost impossible for the recipient to say no. Reports differ from technical articles. So you must use somewhat different writing methods for articles and reports. Always keep in mind the two essentials for good reports—logical organization, and accurate facts.

CHAPTER CHECK-UP

1. Why are reports written? What results are usually sought?
2. How can you ensure getting the action you want from a report?
3. List the kinds of reports used today. Describe each.
4. Show how the contents of a report should differ for various levels of management.
5. What are the five essentials of long-form reports? Discuss each.
6. What five questions do most readers of a report ask?
7. How can you outline your report?
8. What is a good subject sequence for formal reports?
9. Discuss each part of the sequence given in answer to question 8.
10. What can you do to improve your report writing style?
11. List four ways to make reports more interesting. Discuss each.
12. Give six ways of dramatizing a report for your readers.
13. What is a good way to deliver your report?
14. List useful research sources for reports.
15. Summarize the report check list given in this chapter.
16. Discuss the use of a letter of transmittal for reports.

Chapter 12

WRITING INDUSTRIAL AND MILITARY INSTRUCTION MANUALS

Instruction manuals are the main means of communication between equipment builders and users. And the more complex the equipment, the greater the writing task in preparing the manual. If you spend much time in industry you're almost certain to run into an instruction-manual writing job. Let's take a look at some typical manuals and see how they're written. You'll also learn the best ways to write a manual yourself.

WHAT IS AN INSTRUCTION MANUAL?

Most modern instruction manuals tell the reader how to do things—install a machine, maintain a machine, operate one, etc. These manuals give specific how-to instructions. Relatively little theory is covered. The reason why theory is given less attention than other phases of the subject is that instruction-manual readers want quick answers to practical problems they meet.

Users of instruction manuals are often technicians, mechanics, or operating personnel. Some may be highly trained—others may never have seen the machine or device before. So the instructions must be clear, concise, and accurate. Remember—the instruction book you write may be used on an arctic mountain, in a submarine, or on an airplane. Your readers will believe and apply every word in the manual. You must be precise, exact, and above all, *clear*. Instruction-manual writing demands that you continually put yourself in your reader's place. Only then can you anticipate his questions.

157

TYPICAL INSTRUCTION MANUALS

We haven't space here to reproduce an entire instruction manual. But the following paragraphs, chosen from typical manuals, will show you the style of writing used today. Note that all the instructions are specific—they tell the reader *what to do, how to do it, when to do it,* and *why to do it.* Only when you aim at a clear, concise explanation of the job can you expect your reader to understand you.

To test for the opposite polarity of alternating poles, bridge two pole tips with a piece of soft iron. If the polarities of the poles differ, the piece will be strongly attracted, whereas, if the poles are of the same polarity, there will be no attraction. Polarity can be tested by use of a compass, but the compass must not be carried too near the poles, as it may be demagnetized, or even reversed.

The maintenance man should not need to make any mechanical adjustments other than checking brush tension occasionally and replacing brushes correctly. When good commutation cannot be obtained, look over the following mechanical features, trying the commutation after each change, and noting the effect produced:

1. Inspect all connections, and be sure that none is loose.
2. Check the connections and be sure that the commutating field, or any part of it, is not reversed, and that one or more of the main windings are not reversed.
3. Check the brush spacing and alignment. In general, the more accurate the brush spacing, the more uniformly good will be the commutation.
4. Check the mechanical neutral, and try shifting the brushes each way from neutral. Very often a slight shift is advantageous. (In shifting brushes, the question of regulation of speed on the motors, and division of load on the generators, should not be overlooked.)
5. Inspect the brushes and see that they move freely in the holder, and that the pigtails do not interfere with any part of the rigging. Look for burning or roughness of the contact surfaces.
6. Check the pressure, and see that the brush fit is good (see page 199).
7. Inspect the surface of the commutator, and with a canvas wiper, wipe off any blackening. If it is rough or eccentric, causing the

brushes to chatter or move in the holders, it should be ground and perhaps turned. (See page 197.)

8. Check the centering of the commutating poles between the main poles, and check both the main and commutating-pole air gap.[1]

Note that the mechanic is told exactly what to do. (The page numbers in these instructions refer to pages in the actual manual.) On many of the pages referred to in the manual, both line drawings and halftone illustrations *show* the reader how to do his job. So if you want to be a good instructor, you must not only tell the reader what, how, when, and why. *You must also show the reader.* Specific how-to text and clear working drawings and photos are your keys to successful instruction manuals.

Now let's look over portions of another well-written manual: [2]

Grouting the Unit to the Foundation

After the unit has been aligned, pull down on the foundation bolt nuts snugly, and recheck alignment at the coupling and for angular position of the flanges, and adjust if necessary.

Do not hurry the setting and alignment of units on the foundation. A little care and a little more time will give longer and better service from both pump and driver. Build a dam around the foundation with boards as shown in Fig. 18, below.

It is a matter of personal experience and preference whether or not wedges should be removed or grouted under the bedplate. Both methods are apparently successful. If it is desired to remove the wedges after pouring, mark their location before pouring the grout.

A good mixture for grout is one part cement and two parts clean sharp sand, wet enough to flow freely (about the consistency of thick cream), but not so wet that the cement will separate from the sand and float to the surface. Holes are provided in the bedplate to permit pouring of grout under bedplate. They also act as an air vent and permit proper stirring of grout as it is poured. Fill under bedplate completely and stir grout thoroughly under bedplate to break up air pockets. The grout should be from ¾″ to 1½″ thick under the supporting edge of baseplate.

When the grout has thoroughly set and hardened, remove the dam,

[1] From General Electric Company, "How to Maintain Motors and Generators," with permission.

[2] From Ingersoll-Rand Company, "Instructions for Installing and Operating Ingersoll-Rand Centrifugal Pumps," by permission.

and, if desired, remove the wedges. Fill in the holes left by the wedges and trim the edges. Recheck the alignment and if any misalignment is evident, it should be corrected by placing shims under the pump or driver feet. Careful attention to this detail will help prevent hot bearings in both pump and driver.

Troubles . . . If any of the following troubles are encountered, they may be due to the causes listed below:

A. No water delivered—
   1. Pump not primed.
   2. Speed too low. Check motor voltage.
   3. Air leak on suction.
   4. Discharge head too high.
   5. Suction lift too high.
   6. Impeller plugged up.
   7. Wrong direction of rotation.
B. Not enough water delivered—
   1. Air leaks in suction or stuffing box.
   2. Speed too low.
   3. Suction lift too high.
   4. Impeller partially plugged.
   5. Not enough suction head for hot water.
   6. Total head too high.
   7. Pump defects:
      a. Excessive ring clearances.
      b. Damaged impeller.
   8. Suction not submerged enough.

The last two examples show good uses of subheadings and trouble-shooting tabulations. You can make an instruction manual easier to use by inserting subheads where they will help the reader. Use the main subject of a paragraph for the subhead. Try to keep the subheads consistent. For instance, when writing about the components of a machine, use only part names as subheads. Thus in a manual on motors you might use the following subheads: "Shaft," "Bearings," "Frame," "Armature," "Windings," "Enclosures," etc. Note that all these are nouns, and components of a motor.

When discussing operating procedures, choose appropriate words. Typical ones might be: "Greasing," "Oiling," "Starting," "Stopping," "Inspecting," etc. Do not combine words from the component section with those in the operating section, unless they are related. If you must combine the words from the two sections in the operating section, do it this way: "Oiling the shaft," "Greasing the bearings," "Starting the motor," etc. Handling your subheads this way helps the reader understand the instructions and makes them easier to use.

Trouble-shooting tables find a use in almost every instruction manual. For they tell the reader exactly what to look for when trouble develops. Even if your reader does not find the trouble through the items you list, he'll have a good chance of finding it in related items.

If you are not very familiar with the machine or device you're writing about, get expert assistance when preparing trouble-shooting tables. Have a mechanic list every trouble he's met in the unit. Try to classify these troubles under a few major causes, as above. Ask the engineers who designed the machine to do the same. Classify all these troubles. Then have them checked by *both* the mechanic and the engineer.

Send the list out to field engineers, mechanics, and others who know the machine and its problems. Ask for their suggestions. Include these in the table. Don't be afraid of competitive firms picking up your trouble chart and using it against your firm in sales campaigns. They probably have the same troubles—and maybe others you have never heard of.

TYPES OF INSTRUCTION MANUALS

Today you'll meet two major types of instruction manuals—industrial (or commercial) and military. The two types are similar in intent. But the methods used for presentation may be different. In writing a military manual you will usually follow a military specification covering the content and format. Industrial manuals are not written to particular specifications. Each manual is a separate problem and is designed to meet the reader's needs. Since industrial manuals are sometimes effective selling tools, they may be elaborately prepared. Use of two or more colors, foldouts, and other aids is popular today.

Military and commercial manuals may contain as many as five different kinds of information: (1) operating instructions, (2) service instructions, (3) overhaul procedures, (4) parts lists, and (5) development equipment. All this information may be combined in a

single manual, or it may require two or more. In industry the present
trend is to use a single manual wherever possible. But military practice may often require two or more manuals, each covering a separate
function. Here are typical subjects covered under each of the five
divisions of information, and helpful hints for writing about them:

Operating instructions. When writing operating instructions try to
include enough theory and principles of operation to give the operator a fundamental understanding of how to use the equipment intelli-
gently. If you're cramped for space, as you often may be, give greater
attention to principles of operation. For if the operator wants information on theory he can probably find it in a standard reference
book.

Include operating limitations—like maximum and minimum pressures, temperatures, speeds, etc. You can help the operator do a
better job if you include a list of precautions he should observe.

Be sure to cover in detail any adjustments, checks, maintenance,
or emergency procedures he can or should perform. In writing any
instruction manual keep in mind that operating personnel may not
be highly trained. Also, they may not have access to the tools and
special equipment needed for major repairs and maintenance. So
limit your coverage to operating adjustments, unless you are told to
cover more areas.

For some devices and machines, proper warmup and shutdown
procedures are essential operating information. Include all that apply.
And be sure to discuss inspection practices, cleaning, preservation,
and lubrication methods.

Service instructions. These usually cover organizational and field
maintenance. Field servicing is often done by maintenance personnel
who are attached to or employed by the using organization or firm.
So you'll find that field servicing is limited primarily by the tools
and maintenance equipment available in the field. Poorly functioning or unserviceable parts and assemblies are usually not repaired in
the field. Instead they are sent to an overhaul depot or shop for
repair, rebuilding, or both.

When writing service instructions, be sure to include tests and
adjustments coming within the scope of field servicing. Because
service instructions and operating procedures are often similar, they
may be included in the same manual.

Overhaul procedures. The purpose of overhaul instructions is to give detailed information for a major overhaul or complete rebuilding of the equipment. Overhaul shops have more specialized skills and equipment than field service forces.

When writing overhaul instructions for mechanical equipment, try to use exploded views from the parts list. These views help your reader understand the detailed instructions you give on disassembly and reassembly. To make your disassembly instructions easier to understand, number the parts in the exploded views in the disassembly sequence.

Do not omit detailed instructions on how to conduct performance tests of the equipment after overhaul. The only way the operator can check his work is by testing the equipment. So be sure to give him step-by-step ways to perform the tests.

Parts lists. The main purpose of a parts list is to locate and identify parts for replacement purposes. Some specifications for instruction manuals require you to identify, describe, and illustrate all parts; others do not require coverage of standard items like common bolts and nuts. But nearly all military specifications require illustration of parts.

Parts of mechanical equipment are usually shown in exploded views. Each part is shown in a disassembled position. But its relative location with respect to the other parts is also shown.

Figure 12-1 shows a typical parts list. The first item in the parts list is the complete assembly. The component parts follow in the order of disassembly. Often, attaching hardware is listed after the part it attaches and is identified as *attaching parts*. When making up the parts list, be sure that you use the part numbers of the manufacturer. Then there will be no trouble in ordering replacements.

Some military agencies require that you show government stock numbers for the part. When this occurs the manufacturer may be required to submit complete descriptions and drawings of the parts to the stock-numbering agency.

Indent the part and assembly names in the nomenclature column to show the relative order of assembly. For example, the primer (-5) in Fig. 12-1, is indented one space to the right of the fuel primer assembly (-4) to show that it is a part of the fuel primer assembly. The fuel primer assembly, part number B-9119, includes the primer.

But the primer, part number B-11333, also may be procured separately.

Electronic parts list specifications often do not require exploded views or coverage of standard hardware. Photographs of the chassis with all parts intact are used for identification of functional electronic

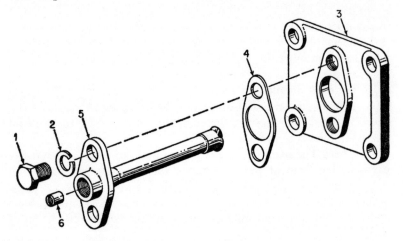

Exploded View of Fuel Primer and Adapter Assembly

Figure & Index No.	Part Number	Nomenclature 1 2 3 4 5 6 7	Units Per Assy
2-	C-9058	Fuel Primer and Adapter Assembly. . .	1
-1	A-9120	. Screw - Mach, hex hd, 0.250-28 NF 3	2
-2	A-9121	. Washer - Spring lock, 0.267 in. ID X 0.057 in. thk, stainless steel.	2
-3	C-9118	. Plate - Adapter	1
-4	ASD-12219	. Gasket.	1
	B-9119	. Primer Assembly - Fuel.	1
-5	B-11333	. . Primer.	1
-6	A-9123	. . Strainer.	1

Fig. 12-1. Typical exploded view and parts list for a manual. (*Courtesy of Product Engineering*)

parts. The reference symbol or part number is shown in the photo or drawing of the equipment. Full parts information can be presented in the parts list. This list is arranged in the order of symbol reference or parts number.

Development equipment. Instruction manuals for development equipment or prototype units are generally special. Only a few copies are needed. Format requirements are usually much less stringent than for manuals covering production items. But this is no reason for your slighting the writing job. Instruction manuals for development equipment are often expanded to full coverage for production units. So the better your initial writing job, the easier it is to write a finished manual.

Differences in manuals. Commercial and industrial operating, instruction, and maintenance manuals have the same objectives as military manuals. But, depending on the complexity of the equipment, the breakdowns may not be so fine, as far as the classifications are concerned. Sometimes the user's instruction manual and the serviceman's maintenance manual can be combined into one. But a parts replacement list is nearly always needed in commercial and industrial manuals.

HOW TO ORGANIZE THE WRITING JOB

Preparation of instruction manuals can rarely be done satisfactorily if assigned to an individual in the engineering department in addition to his regular duties. Besides the time involved, close association with the equipment often prevents the objective viewpoint needed in writing for a different level of technical knowledge or aptitude. The task should be performed by competent engineering and technical writers and illustrators headed up by responsible personnel.

You must make a comprehensive analysis of the job before starting work. Here are seven pre-writing steps:

1. Determine fully the contractual requirements. If you have any questions concerning what is to be done, or how, *ask them at once—not later.*

2. Gather all the available source material. Include all applicable specifications and up-to-date equipment data. Arrange your material in an orderly manner for easy reference. If the equipment is in the development stage, arrange to receive notification of design changes.

3. Read and understand clearly the specifications set up for your job. These may be either commercial or military specs. You can avoid costly errors by understanding the specs from the start.

4. Study the equipment. Prepare a systematic breakdown of the assembly and subassembly components. Make certain that your analy-

sis of the parts is in keeping with the specs governing the job. You'll
find it is usually a good idea to do the parts list first, since the parts
information is needed for writing the other material. And do not
overlook supplementary equipment like accessories, test equipment,
special service tools, and connecting cables. Your component breakdown not only helps you establish a presentation sequence—it also
aids you in making a comprehensive evaluation of the job ahead.

5. Prepare a detailed outline. Like any other writing job, a good
instruction manual cannot be written without an outline.

6. Check with the man who will approve or disapprove the final
manual. He'll welcome a chance to discuss the manual before actual
writing starts. These discussions will always save time, trouble, money,
and energy.

7. Establish a schedule and a budget for your writing job. The
schedule sets a series of mileposts or check points for evaluating job
progress. Assign target dates for the completion of each of the phases
so that the final delivery date will be met. Include a contingency
factor in the schedule for the unforeseen developments that always
happen.

The same principles apply to a budget. Make equitable allocations
in hours (or in dollars if cost-accounting service is available) for each
operation. Keeping job cards or sheets for each operation, on which
time is recorded, is a convenient means of checking time expenditures.
You'll learn that you cannot emphasize too strongly that, as with the
schedule, contingency allowances must be included in budgeting.

Writing. The actual writing is not simple. Good technical writing
is more than skimming through the subject matter and setting down
points that occur to the writer. Good writing comes only from much
study and careful consideration of the needs of eventual users and
from thorough organization of your material. *You must use an outline.* Suggestions for writing and illustrating the instruction manual
are given below.

The need for you to understand the eventual user is fundamental.
You must present all the information at his reading level. The
reading level for most instruction manuals should be that of a second-
year high school student. A typical user also can be expected to have
a minimum of technical background and no previous experience with
the equipment. Overhaul instruction manual readers can be assumed

to have considerably more technical background with other equipment, but none with the equipment covered by the manual.

WRITING, ILLUSTRATING, AND PRODUCING THE MANUAL

Writing. Here are nine hints you can use when writing industrial, commercial, and military instruction manuals. Try to use as many of these hints as possible whenever you write any kind of manual.

1. Use short sentences.
2. Use short paragraphs and a separate paragraph for each thought.
3. Give specific instructions. Statements such as "Test in accordance with authorized shop procedure" are worthless unless the source of such procedures is given.
4. Avoid uncommon words, unnecessary technical phraseology, and words peculiar to a single industry.
5. Avoid complicated phrasing. Delete superfluous words.
6. Use exact nomenclature. Name each part, component, or subassembly. Do not use such references as "the unit."
7. Divide the text by appropriate headings and subheadings.
8. Tie in discussion and illustrations so that one follows closely on the other.
9. Edit the manual. Instruction books are teaching devices and as such deserve proper presentation.

Illustrations. Good illustrations are just as important as good text. So never skimp on illustrations. The better your photos and drawings the greater the chance of quick acceptance and active use of the manual. Keep the following hints in mind when you prepare illustrations.

Photographs

1. Photographs may be used for equipment views, operational views, and parts identification.
2. Photographs usually require retouching to retain detail sharpness and contrast.
3. Eliminate superfluous or unattractive backgrounds by cropping and retouching or opaquing.
4. Use exploded views to identify parts in mechanical assemblies and assembled chassis views for electronic equipment.
5. Identify parts by number, reference symbol, or name on the picture.

6. For identification nomenclature use copy prepared by typesetting or with mechanical lettering guides.

7. Plan each picture, and supply the photographer with a rough layout so that each view covers required subject matter.

Line Drawings

1. For wiring diagrams and electrical schematics, use consistent practices on symbols, line weights, conventions, and layouts as recommended by the industry or military service involved.

2. Use mechanical schematic drawings to illustrate operating features and maintenance practices. Present hydraulic, pneumatic, and mechanical drive systems in schematic form.

3. Specify plan views to show installation and mounting features, lubrication practices, equipment outlines and dimensions, and panel markings.

4. Simplify the job of explaining operating and maintenance details by liberal use of pictorial drawings (Fig. 12-2). Isometric projection is common, but dimetric and trimetric projection gives the subject a more natural appearance. Shade them when it will add realism.

5. Use exploded views in conjunction with parts lists to show assembly and disassembly procedures. Use pictorial drawing technique.

6. Limit the use of color to functional purpose such as flow diagrams, etc.

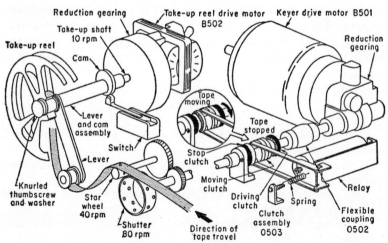

Fig. 12-2. Pictorial view for a manual. (*Courtesy of Product Engineering*)

Production. Today many technical writers are assigned the task of supervising the production of the manuals they write. If this occurs in your case, you can avoid difficulty by following these suggestions:

1. Type the manuscript double-spaced on white paper. Leave wide margins, and adhere to precise standards on punctuation, format, style, and abbreviations.
2. Proofread each typed copy for accuracy; usually a rough draft, approval draft, and final draft are necessary.
3. Mark the final draft for type, spacing, and make-up. Make all changes and corrections in the manuscript prior to starting final typography.
4. Make certain that the index, contents pages, title pages, appendix, and other data are supplied with the manuscript.
5. Proofread the reproduction copy—in both galley and rough page form—and check placement of and references to tables and illustrations.
6. Schedule printing well in advance to ensure delivery when required.

CHECK LIST FOR INSTRUCTION MANUALS

Instruction manuals vary so much that it is impossible to set up a typical outline, as we did for articles. However, you'll find the following check list helpful. Essentially it is a listing of almost every subject item and production need you'll meet in writing and producing a manual.

To use this list, just check the topics you'd like to include. Add any others that are peculiar to the subject. Then you'll have a good outline to guide your writing. And when you write, be clear and direct. Use the active voice wherever possible. Items listed under "Description," "Operation," "Theory," and "Maintenance" may occur in one manual after another. So use this list regularly. Keep it on your desk while you write. Delete those topics that do not apply to your manual.

Description

What is this information	Price
Purpose of this information	Reordering
How to use this information	Order, shipment, contract numbers
Other publications required	Shipping list
Illustration of equipment	Shipping damage report
Identify manufacturer	Reshipping requirements

Equipment name and number
Manufacturer's guarantee
Relate to other models
Relate to associated equipment
Modifications available
If system, what are units?
If in larger system, explain
What does equipment do?
What goes in?
What happens to it?
What comes out?
Why do it this way?
What is equipment used with?
Where, when, why is it used?
Who uses it?
Advantages of the equipment
Limitations of the equipment
Advertising of product(s)
Advertising of company

Accessories supplied
Accessories not supplied
Basic principle of operation
List characteristics
List controls
List connectors
List cables
Power requirements
Weight and dimensions
Operating supplies required
Installation requirements
Operator requirements
Weatherproofing
Tropicalization
Warnings and precautions
If system: repeat for each unit
Note patent numbers
Give copyright date
Notes on government licensing

Operation

Repeat from preceding as needed
Write to operator's level
Operator requirements
Illustrations of what operator sees
Identify panel controls
Unpacking
Installation requirements
Installation procedures
Intercabling drawings, tables, schematics
Identify by name and number
Tabulate modes of operation
When are different modes used?
How it operates, control-wise
Operational block diagrams
Enough theory for operator
Pre-operational adjustments
Turning on the equipment
Connecting: inputs, outputs, accessory equipment

Standby operation
Operating the equipment
Emergency operation
Turning off the equipment
Post-operational adjustments
Keeping log of operation
Local and remote operation
Warnings, precautions
Supplies needed
Replacing supplies
Repeat above for each mode
Define unusual expressions
Explain unusual procedures
Refer to technician's adjustments
Operator's tests for operation
Operator's maintenance check chart
Fuse, tube, vibrator, crystal, indicator and plug-in-unit replacement table

Theory

Repeat from preceding as needed
Write to reader's level
How it works, not why
What goes in?
What happens to it?
What comes out?
Compare with familiar equipment
Differences between models
Diagrams: systems block, unit block, vector, simplified schematic, complete schematic, primary power distribution

Oscilloscope wave patterns
Wave-shape comparison chart
Signal-flow analysis
System-operation theory
Unit-by-unit theory
Stage-by-stage theory
Theory: by functions performed
Theory: output toward input
Mathematical basis of operation
Theory: each mode of operation

Preventive Maintenance

Repeat from preceding as needed
Write to technician's level
Technician requirements
Check-chart for proper operation
Maintenance check-chart
Lubrication chart
Hydraulic maintenance chart
Periodical checks (hourly, daily, etc., through annual)
How gain access for maintenance
Periodic overhaul procedures
Precautions, warnings
Special test circuits
Special test setups
Safety precautions
Re-tropicalization

Re-weatherproofing
Specify lubricants
List special tools
List special equipment
Tube, fuse, vibrator, indicator, crystal and plug-in-unit locations
Pre-maintenance procedures
Post-maintenance procedures
Cleaning, painting, polishing
Corrosion: rust, water, salt-spray damage; air-filter, cable, connector check
Parts-replacement schedule
Where to buy replacements parts
Supply replacement schedule
Where to buy supplies

Corrective Maintenance

Repeat from preceding as needed
Write to technician's level
Technician requirements
Recommended maintenance approach
Illustrations of equipment

Overhaul procedures
Mechanical disassembly drawings
Mechanical reassembly drawings
Accessory equipment required
Special tools required
List faults and probable causes

Component identification charts, drawings and photos
Trouble-shooting output to input
Trouble-shooting input to output
Trouble-shooting: for system, by unit, at controls, by symptoms, by test points, by test signal
Signal tracing chart
Charts: oscilloscope wave-form, voltage, resistance
Diagrams: servicing block, simplified schematic, over-all schematic, unit-by-unit schematic, vector, primary power
Mechanical exploded views

Special test circuits
Illustrations showing adjustments
Mechanical, hydraulic pneumatic, electrical servicing
Disassembly, reassembly
Emergency repair
Voltages on schematic drawings
Wave-shapes on schematic drawings
List of component parts
Parts manufacturers
Parts ordering
Repair: cabinet, corrosion, rust, water damage

Things to Remember

Covering letter
Get your company's name on it
Get your name on it
Give date, department
Type one side, double spaced
Drawings, pictures are better than words
Hold consistent nomenclature
Hold consistent technical level
Will it be understood?
Write to reader's level
Write to reader's interests

Check security clearance
Table of contents
List of illustrations
List of tables
Number the pages
Use short words
Use simple sentences
Keep paragraphs brief
White space for easy reading
Step-by-step procedures best
File a reference copy
Keep a copy yourself

SUMMARY

Industrial and military instruction manuals are important in every field today. Since the users of instruction manuals often do not have much technical training, careful writing is a must. A good instruction manual tells the reader what to do, how to do it, when to do it, why to do it. And if possible, the manual should *show* the reader how to do his job. Good illustrations are important in every instruction manual. Clear organization of the writing job is important. A good instruction manual cannot be written without an outline.

CHAPTER CHECK-UP

1. What is an instruction manual? What types of readers use these manuals?
2. Why are instruction manuals important? What is their main purpose?
3. Choose two examples of manufacturer's instruction manuals. Study them and make a list of their good and poor features. How could the poor features be improved?
4. What are the outstanding characteristics of well-written instruction manuals?
5. How can subheadings and trouble-shooting tabulations be used in instruction manuals?
6. Make up a list of difficulties you might meet in writing an instruction manual. Classify these troubles and tabulate them in a typical instruction-manual list.
7. How can you secure data for a trouble-shooting list? How can you check the data in this list?
8. List five types of instruction manuals. Describe the purpose of each. What kind of information should each contain?
9. What is a parts list? How should it be assembled? Give an example of a typical parts list.
10. Give seven pre-writing steps for instruction manuals. Discuss each step.
11. Why should the writing schedule and budget be given careful study?
12. Give nine pointers for writing instruction manuals. Discuss each.
13. What items should you remember when preparing photos for an instruction manual? When preparing line drawings?
14. Give six hints for producing instruction manuals.
15. How can you outline an instruction manual? Prepare an outline for an instruction manual covering (*a*) a selected electronic device, (*b*) a mechanical unit of your choice.

Chapter 13

WRITING INDUSTRIAL AND MILITARY TRAINING MANUALS

Training manuals are used by industrial firms and military agencies in educational activities. These manuals present a basic introduction to a subject. Most training manuals today are prepared for personnel who will operate, service, overhaul, or maintain equipment of some kind. Modern training manuals specialize in clear, concise writing, expertly selected illustrations, and neat, serviceable bindings. So if you expect to write a training manual, be prepared to do the best job you can. Use the suggestions in this chapter to save time and trouble.

There are six steps you must take when writing any training manual. These are: (1) Organize and outline the subject of the manual. (2) Plan the various parts of the manuscript so that it will be a coherent unit. (3) Write the first draft. (4) Choose the illustrations. (5) Polish the text. (6) Send the final copy and illustrations to the production department.

ORGANIZE AND OUTLINE

To organize your writing job, first choose a preliminary content for the manual. This will often be given you when you're assigned the writing task. To narrow the content down to a workable subject you may have to alter the preliminary content slightly. If you must select the preliminary content yourself, then (*a*) determine the purpose of the manual, (*b*) select a working title, and (*c*) make a preliminary list of topics.

Determine the purpose of the manual. Ask why the manual is being written. There are two common reasons why manuals are written—none is available on the subject, or those that are available are outmoded or unsuitable. Your writing task is often more difficult when no manuals are available, because old manuals can provide ideas and material.

Once you know the *why* of a manual, determine the *what.* What will the readers and users expect to get from this manual? Write the answer on a slip of paper and keep it in front of you while you write the manual. Then there's less chance of your writing wandering from the subject.

Select a working title. Your title must define the area within which you'll confine your attention. So choose your working title carefully. The subject given you may be too general for a manual of the length requested.

Suppose you are given the assignment to write a training manual on "Diesel Engines for Generator Drive in Arctic Regions." Engines for this service can be large or small, portable or semiportable, light-duty or heavy-duty, air-injection or solid-injection, etc. To cover all these engines in a single manual of usable size would be very difficult.

So determine what kinds of engines are to be covered. Let's say they are portable, light-duty, solid-injection 10-hp units. The title of your manual then might be "Ten-hp Light-duty Portable Diesel Engines for Arctic Service." The solid-injection feature is omitted because no small engines are built any other way. Certainly the second title is far more specific than the first. And it clearly defines the subject area of your writing.

Make a preliminary topic list. Once you've chosen your working title you're ready to start choosing topics for your manual. Ask yourself: What should my readers learn from this manual? What should they know when they've completed it? What subject areas *must* be covered? What subject areas *might* be covered? How much material can my readers absorb while using this manual? What are the objectives of this manual?

Make notes as you answer these questions. These notes will be the beginning of a list of topics. While you're making this list, talk to other writers who have worked on the same subject. Visit instructors who are teaching in the subject area; sit in on some class discussions and demonstrations.

If the training manual is new, talk to the persons who decided it was needed. Read the pertinent directives and correspondence. And if this is a training manual for the military, check all pertinent specifications. Neglecting this may cause you endless misery.

If you're writing a revision of an existing manual, look over the previous editions. Study them to see which topics they included. Make sure that you'll cover the topics which must be treated, that you'll add those which may have been omitted earlier but are important for the reader, and that you omit those previously treated but not now needed. Also, check those sections containing outdated information.

The topics you list at this stage of your work will probably become the major area of treatment once you begin to outline. So as you make your notes, always keep in mind both your immediate and your ultimate objective.

Once you have your preliminary topic list, you're ready to start research. This is how you'll find many additional important facts for your manual. Remember that the entire contents of the manual will stem from your knowledge and research. Only through adequate research can you be certain to secure accurate information for your readers. To get better results from your research: (1) use your personal experience, (2) get information from conference, and (3) study published and written materials.

Use your personal experience. By seeing, hearing, and experiencing you get a feeling of being at home with your subject. But don't be misled into thinking that personal experience is the only knowledge you need. You may tend to ride your pet experiences and neglect other factors that are just as essential to the manual. If you are experienced in one area and intend to include that area in a training manual, give it only the amount of space it deserves. Fill in your background with experience from other sources.

Get information from conference. Conferences with authorities on your subject often provide you with excellent data. Discussion with such people may bring out points which you have forgotten or points which you tend to minimize but they feel are important because of their past experiences. Most of these people will gladly cooperate with you. But, as with personal experience and observations, you must carefully weigh what you hear. The human element makes a person stress his own experience and neglect areas about which he knows little.

Study published and written materials. The next avenue of research, printed and typed documents, almost always offers you information you might not be able to get otherwise. Almost every industrial firm and military base has a library—often with special-subjects sources. No matter how well you know your subject, you are not being fair to your potential readers unless you consult the available source material.

Go to printed sources—books, catalogs, technical orders, regulations, specifications, old manuals; read everything you can find on your subject. Learn about the topics you'll write on. Prepare yourself to ask meaningful questions when you have an interview or go out to watch operations.

Make notes on 3 by 5 or 5 by 7 cards when you find usable information. Key each card with its reference source. This method helps you keep an orderly record of your reading. It acts as an aid when you are ready to start organizing your data into an outline. In this way you will be able not only to give the proper credit to sources but to go back to a source if your notes are incomplete.

With your research finished, you are ready to begin your outline. Properly prepared, the outline—often called the writer's map—tells you where you are going and how you will get there. It marks a point of beginning, predetermines the steps along the way, and clearly identifies the destination.

Make a good guiding outline. By an outline we don't mean a skimpy listing of one- or two-word topics in which the subjects are vague in the author's mind—and will consequently be devoid of concrete meaning to the reader. We mean a valid, explanatory listing of the topics to be discussed. These topics should be arranged in an order that unifies the writing and makes it coherent.

Select useful topics. Perhaps the best way to explain how to prepare a good outline is to take one that is almost useless and actually revise it into an outline you can follow. We can start with the following skimpy outline of a writer's manual:

Guide to Writing
1. *Introduction*
   a. Purpose
   b. Scope
   c. Plan
2. *On writing*
   a. Paragraphs
   b. Sentences
   c. Words
   d. Verbs
3. *On illustrating*
4. *On organizing*
   a. Making plans
   b. Outlining
5. *Beginnings and endings*
6. *Editing*

If you stretch your imagination, you can see that this list of topics covers the general subject of how to write training manuals. But it isn't clear and specific enough to help a writer, regardless of his experience with the subject. A person qualified to write about writing would scrap this skimpy list and start all over again.

Now let's take this poor example and improve it:

How to Prepare Industrial and Military Training Manuals

I. *You must first organize and outline*
   A. Make preliminary content selection
      1. Determine purpose and scope
      2. Choose a working title
      3. Make preliminary list of topics
   B. Conduct necessary research
      1. Use personal experience
      2. Get information from conference
      3. Study published and written materials
         a. Use up-to-date official publications
         b. Consult reliable catalog sources

    C. Make a guiding outline
      1. Select useful topics
      2. Arrange topics into a writing map
    D. Let's repeat: Organize and outline your work
  II. *The manuscript should be a coherent unit*
    A. Interest readers with a good beginning
    B. Make the writing flow smoothly
      1. Bridge gaps with good transitions
      2. Use relationship-showing devices
      3. Write paragraphs readers can understand
      4. Introduce new ideas with topic sentences
      5. Mark ends of thoughts with summary sentences
    C. End your writing with a terminal that teaches
    D. Plan the coherence and unity of the manuscript
 III. *Write the first draft*
    A. Help your readers understand you
      1. Find out what readers already know
      2. Learn the students' reading ability
      3. Decide how much material to give the reader
      4. Interest the reader: Talk directly to him
    B. Write in a lively, readable style
      1. Use words familiar to the reader
      2. Use concrete words
      3. Choose action verbs that appeal to readers
      4. Write effective sentences
        a. Write shorter sentences; observe content
        b. Steer clear of inversions
        c. Cut down number of parenthetical expressions
        d. Go easy with short, choppy sentences
        e. Be cautious with fragments
      5. Personalize: Get reader into the act
    C. Do a thorough job of writing first draft
 IV. *Industrial and military training literature frequently needs illustrations*
    A. Pick the passages to be illustrated
    B. Choose illustrations for your text
    C. Integrate illustrations and text
      1. Put illustrations into text
      2. Refer to illustrations
      3. Discuss illustrations in text

      D. Prepare illustrations for use
          1. Label all necessary parts
          2. Give illustrations good talking captions
          3. Determine size of final copy
      E. Work with illustrator
      F. Decide when to use color with illustrations
      G. Again: Make illustrations help text
   V. *Writers should rework manuscripts*
      A. Appraise manuscripts for content and approach
      B. Reorganize and rework manuscript
      C. Edit what you have written
          1. Have complete and accurate material
          2. Make sure manuscript is clear, coherent unit
      D. Evaluate readability of manuscript
          1. Measure with Flesch scale of readability
          2. Consider the Fog count
          3. Check mechanics and grammar
             a. Common errors
             b. A few reminders about punctuation
      E. Let's say it again: rework your manuscript
  VI. *Prepare copy and art work for reproduction*
      A. How to make up a dummy
      B. Method of preparing line copy
          1. Ways to type the text
          2. How to make direct image plates
          3. Methods of marking headings and other topics
          4. How to handle line-copy illustrations
      C. Methods of preparing tone copy
          1. Photograph types
          2. Cropping photographs
          3. Preparing finished halftones
      D. How to paste up for camera-readiness
      E. Repeat: Get copy and artwork ready for reproduction

Note the difference between the entries in the second outline and those in the first. The summary type of topics used in the improved version tells the writer specifically how he should slant his text. And when used in the manual the summary type tells the reader what he will find in the text.

Also note that the topic entries are telegraphic sentences. In your own writing you can use similar types of entries, or you may prefer noun-phrase entries like:

Sentences that appeal to readers
The plan of presentation
Transitions that bridge thought gaps

It doesn't matter which you use. But be consistent with topics of equal value. All main headings should have similar construction; so should subheadings, and sub-subheadings.

So far as the actual type of topic is concerned, you can use three distinct types: the informational, the instructional, and the directive. The informational type, like a newspaper headline, summarizes the information:

Landing ships supported Normandy invasion
Outlines help maintain unity

The instructional topic is phrased like these:

A method for cleaning oil filters
How to remove the B-52 nose wheel
The way to edit your writing

These topics are usually helpful when you're explaining techniques and procedures. But if you use this type, don't monotonously repeat "how to."

Directive topics can be helpful when you're teaching how-to-do. Note these examples that give specific directions:

Remove the B-52 nose wheel
Revise what you've written
Avoid stilted phrases
Give captions specific wording

The purpose of the material you're writing will help you decide the type of topic to use. But no matter which type you need, try to make each one as specific and clear as possible.

Main-heading outline. At times you may find it easier to prepare two outlines, the first containing only the main headings, the second containing both the main headings and all the subheadings.

Why prepare two outlines? Well, the first, or main-heading, outline enables you to develop the principal areas of your subject matter.

Since these areas must be chosen *before* you choose your subtopics, it
is easier for you to alter your outline in this stage. Here is a main-
heading outline for "The Submarine," produced by the Standards
and Curriculum Branch Training Division, Bureau of Naval Personnel:

1. Development of the submarine
2. Submarine definitions and terminology
3. Elementary principles of submarine buoyancy and stability
4. Compartmentation and exterior installations
5. Tank arrangements
6. The engineering plant
7. Air supply and exhaust
8. Refrigeration and air-conditioning systems
9. Water system
10. The trim and drain systems
11. Air systems
12. Fuel and lubricating oil system
13. Hydraulic system
14. Anchor handling gear and capstans
15. The snorkel system
16. Compensation and reballasting

Each of these headings represents a chapter in the published
manual. These sixteen chapters have a total of 87 subheadings. As
you can see, it would be far easier to work first with the main topics
than with these and the 87 subtopics.

It is interesting to note how the subject matter of this training
manual is related to that of the other manuals in the series to which
it belongs. The eleven training manuals in this series have the following titles:

"The Submarine" (chapter list given above)
"Submarine Main Propulsion Diesels"
"Submarine Electrical Installations"
"Submarine Refrigerating and Air-conditioning Systems"
"Submarine Air Systems"
"Submarine Periscope Manual"
"Submarine Sonar Operator's Manual"
"Submarine Underwater Log Systems"
"Submarine Hydraulic Systems"

"Submarine Distilling Systems"
"Torpedo Tubes, 24-inch, Submerged, Mks 32 to 39"

Note how the title of each manual defines the area covered. There is no doubt as to where the manual starts and where it stops. These specific titles and subject areas are in complete agreement with the recommendation—*Your title must define the area within which you'll confine your attention.*

Here is another example of a main-heading outline. It is taken from "Helicopter Maintenance Training," prepared by the Air Training Command, Department of the Air Force:

1. History of helicopter development
2. Helicopter aerodynamics
3. Mechanics' tools, aircraft hardware, and safetying
4. Airframes, landing gear and brakes
5. Maintenance publications and supply catalogs
6. Rotor systems
7. Flight controls
8. Power transmission systems
9. Power plants and related systems
10. Aircraft electrical systems
11. Helicopter instruments
12. Helicopter utility systems
13. Aircraft inspection system
    Glossary

Each of these main headings represents a chapter in the published manual. And each chapter has a large number of subheadings. These subheads are chosen, as described above, after the writer is satisfied that the major headings adequately cover his subject.

Arrange your topics into a writing map. Clarity of topics is not the only standard for a good outline. If you want a guide that will show you where you're going, you must arrange the topics into a clear writer's map. You must plan your presentation so the reader can understand your explanations in the order you give them.

With some subjects you can present the material in a historical or chronological sequence. With such a sequence, you present the facts according to the time of occurrence. Thus a training manual on atomic energy might start with the first experiments in the nineteenth century and proceed to the developments of the twentieth century.

A manual that tells a man how to do a particular job may follow this method also. If you want your reader to take each step—first, second, third—you'll help him if you present the material according to an enumerated plan.

Another method of presentation is to give the reader all the facts without using the time-of-occurrence plan. For instance, you may be teaching readers the various systems that operate in an internal-combustion reciprocating engine. To help him understand the information, you may explain in general terms how the whole engine works. Then you break up the explanation into various parts and treat each system separately—the fuel system, the electrical system, the cooling system, etc. (Note how closely this resembles the submarine and helicopter manuals outlined above.) After you've treated all the topics, you may bring them together again.

Some people call this method the *whole-part-whole plan* of presentation; others call it the *logical-arrangement plan*. Whatever the tag, remember that this method gives the whole story but does not indicate where emphasis is to be placed.

Some writers like to present material in a *most-important-to-least-important* pattern. Others like the *what's-to-be-done, why-it's-to-be-done, how-it's-to-be-done* sequence. Either method may work successfully; but if you intend to apply one of them to your own writing, be sure it will fit your subject.

Some people call these *easy-to-difficult, known-to-unknown,* and *most-important-to-least-important* methods *psychological methods* of arrangement. Others simply say they help you use the logical approach. But again, the name does not matter. The important point with regard to these various methods—as well as those previously mentioned —is that you, the writer, must decide how to present material to your reader. When you arrange your topics in the outline, follow the pattern which best serves the needs of your readers.

MAKE THE MANUAL A COHERENT UNIT

The plan you developed into an outline has been established to make the writing one continuous, coherent whole. If it has been properly arranged you should have a clear guide for the job. Now let's take a look at how you should begin your manual, what to do to bridge gaps, and how to end the manual. Right handling of these problems will make your manual the coherent unit the outline sets up.

Interest the reader with a good lead. Introduce the reader to the subject immediately. Don't waste time with matters of no interest to your readers. Introducing your subject immediately helps you establish unity and coherence. At the same time it focuses your reader's attention on the subject. Here are the leads from the two manuals whose main-heading outlines were given above:

Early Underwater Devices

1A1. Early Greek Devices. The submarine first became a major factor in naval warfare during World War I, when Germany demonstrated its full potentialities. However, its advent at that time, marked by wholesale sinkings of Allied shipping, was in reality the culmination of a long process of development.

Ancient history includes occasional records of attempts at underwater operations in warfare. The Athenians are said to have used divers to clear the entrance to the harbor of Syracuse during the siege of that city. In his operations against Tyre, Alexander the Great ordered divers to impede or destroy any submarine defenses the city might undertake to build. But in none of these records is there a direct reference to the use of submersible apparatus of any kind. There is, however, a legend that Alexander the Great himself made a descent into the sea in a device which kept its occupants dry and admitted light.

The Urge to Fly Is Old

Since the dawn of recorded history there is evidence of man's dream to fly. Long before the goal was achieved, he yearned to soar, like the birds he observed, high above the earth. For centuries this desire remained unfulfilled; it has been realized, for all practical purposes, only within the last 50 years. The theory of helicopter flight is not new, though little was heard about it until the end of World War II. Its development into a workable flying machine is quite recent, dating back only about 15 years. And only during the Korean war did this odd-shaped flying machine come into its own by proving itself a dependable workhorse of the armed forces. Actually, however, the concept of rotary wing flight had its beginnings hundreds of years ago. You can become a better helicopter mechanic if you know something of its beginnings and early history.

Note how each of these leads is an integral part of the whole manual. Both arouse the reader's interest. Further on, the lead explains the purpose of the entire manual, tells the scope, and outlines the plan of presentation. Some manuals do this in the preface, others in the lead.

A good lead helps you introduce your reader to the subject. But the lead alone cannot develop a continuous flow of thought throughout the manual. You'll have to use the other methods and devices we've mentioned. Let's take a look at them.

Make your writing flow smoothly. Facts alone don't make a manual coherent. You must lead from one explanation to another in a way that doesn't confuse your readers. To do this, bridge the gaps between the parts of your manual with good transitions. See Chapter 7 for a discussion of transitions and their use.

Use relationship-showing devices. Besides transitional words and phrases you can use other relationship-showing devices to connect sentences and ideas. For example, you'll often find use for words showing *cause and effect*:

A mechanic first accelerates the engine until it is turning up between 1150 and 1250 rpm. This speed should put the oil pressure just above normal and should make the ammeter show a steady charge.

Many writers like to use *comparisons*, especially when explaining a piece of equipment that may be new to the reader:

A lubricant in an engine is usually thick and stiff on a cold morning; because of this fact, you should give the engine time to warm up so that the oil will get to all working parts. You can compare cold motor oil to cold lard used for frying. When you take the can out of the ice box and put a spoonful in a cold skillet, it remains in a lump and contacts only one part of the pan; but once you turn on the heat, the lump melts and the lard covers all the skillet's surface.

Still another way to relate ideas is by *contrast*:

The writer who prepares a clear outline before he begins any part of his first draft usually comes up with a well planned coherent manuscript. On the other hand, the writer who attempts to write without an explicit guide usually finds when he has finished that his writing has wandered pointlessly from topic to topic.

Often a writer shows relationship by *giving a rule and then pointing out an exception to it*:

In almost all other electrical-circuit maintenance problems, you will have meters to help you find the source of trouble. With this particular type of equipment, however, you will have to use the trial-and-error method of trouble shooting because as yet no special test equipment is available.

These aren't the only means you can use to achieve unity in your writing; the more you write, the more methods you will find for relating ideas and tying thoughts into a coherent whole. But these examples will serve as a guide; using them as a base, you can create or develop your own schemes to link sentences and paragraphs.

Write paragraphs the reader can understand. Coherence of sentences and ideas, however, is only the first step toward making one unit out of a piece of writing. Although sentences are the basic structures, these in turn must be bundled into expressive paragraphs that are within the grasp of the reader.

In determining the scope of your paragraphs, remember your specific audience. Some readers, because of age, education, or background, can accept more material at one moment of concentration than others can. In other words, the length of your paragraphs, as well as the style within the paragraphs, should match the reader's level. Often writers fail to consider this factor; they feel that by keeping their words easy and their sentences simple they are doing all that is needed. That just is not so. Although we read sentences, we focus our attention on the paragraph package. If we are forced to read over too long an interval, we lose relationships and so do not get the full gist of the text.

You must do more, however, than keep paragraphs down to acceptable lengths. Vary the paragraph pattern: scatter long, short, and middle-sized units throughout your writing. This irregularity gives writing eye appeal and holds reader interest.

Since we want readers to concentrate on the writing, what, besides length of a paragraph, will help us get this attention? Four guides will help you hold your audience: (1) Focus the reader's attention as sharply as possible on the topic of the paragraph. (2) Keep all sentences within a paragraph related to the topic. (3) Keep the sentences related to each other so that the reader will have a steady chain of ideas to lead him through the paragraph. (4) Use some kind of signal or summary device at the end of several paragraphs to let the reader know there is a breathing spell just ahead.

The second and third points should be clear enough. But the topic sentence and the summary need further treatment.

Introduce new ideas with topic sentences. A topic phrase or sentence introducing a paragraph tells the reader what the paragraph covers. In a sense, it says to him: "In this paragraph our subject is. . . ." Consider these examples:

A vehicle operator, during his day's operations, keeps certain records and forms. [The paragraph describes the forms and records which the operator keeps.]

A line cut is made from a black-and-white drawing of lines and parts of lines. [The paragraph completely explains a line cut.]

Before you begin writing, organize your material into an outline. [The paragraph describes how to make an outline.]

All too often, especially in industrial and military writing, writers tend to rely on topic headings to identify a paragraph subject. Such use may save words. But experience proves that readers skip or skim over these headings and thus miss the point of the paragraph's early sentences. To test a piece of writing, cover all the headings, and read only the text. If what you read is not clear, then the material needs revising so that the reader will not have to rely on devices he may normally skip.

Once the reader's attention has been focused on the topic sentence, the other sentences should hold together coherently and keep that attention for as long as it takes to cover the point. Active words, easily read sentences, and relationship-showing devices all work together toward this end.

Mark the end of thoughts with summary sentences. Once you have exploited the topic, or once you are ready to move from a major point to a specific supporting minor one, indicate your intentions to the reader. By using some direction-giving sentence, phrase, or device, let the reader know that the time has come for a pause.

In longer paragraphs, you may indicate such a pause by a summary sentence:

By looking back, then, we see that the growth of the Air Force has come about through the combined forces of legislation, evolution, and the keen foresight of certain air-minded military leaders.

A shorter paragraph may be rounded out this way:

Once the mechanic has replaced these plugs, he is ready to start the engine. [The paragraph is about replacing plugs.]

Or perhaps this way:

Finally, you make out the bibliography cards and are ready to start organizing.

You may use devices like these, or you may use methods more in keeping with your own style of writing. But whatever you use, try to give the reader an indication that he may take a deep breath before going on.

End your writing with an effective terminal. After each part, chapter, or section of your manuscript, end the material with a well-written terminal section. In the past, this section has been called a summary; but all too often it has turned out to be nothing more than a sentence form of the table of contents.

Rather than this type of ending, training-manual writers should use one of two distinct types of terminals, the informational or the instructional. Both are bird's-eye views of the material which they terminate. In these terminals you condense the material so tightly that one sentence may synopsize two or three full pages of text.

If you are writing indoctrination or information type of material, use a simple conclusion or informational terminal, one that brings all the topics together in a digest form. The following summary of a chapter on "Building Military Housing Units" illustrates this type of terminal:

A military housing unit has 8″ × 16″ footings, with cinder block or masonry foundations built up at least two feet off the ground. It has 2 × 10 floor joists set on 16″ centers, and it has 2 × 4 studs set on 24″ centers. Ceiling joists are 24″ apart and are usually 2 × 6s. Rafters also are 2 × 6's and tied to the joists so that they project at least 18 inches out from the sides of the structure.

Most housing units use regular 1 × 8 drop siding, though asbestos siding may be substituted where cost and labor permit. Roof decking, however, should be 1 × 6 or 1 × 8, whichever is available.

Interior walls should be made of sheetrock properly taped so that no cracks remain. Flooring should be 1 × 4 tongue-in-groove pine, sanded to a smooth finish.

Doors should all be of a standard size, preferably 2′ 8″ × 6′ 8″; and windows ought to be the standard 6-over-6 type. The roof of a military housing unit should be either 210 or 220, thick-butt shingles (unless metal roofs are specified because of weather conditions).

Notice how specific facts make this kind of an ending mean something to the readers. Statements like these will refresh the reader and will do a good job of tying all loose ends together.

The second type of ending recommended for manuals, guides, and pamphlets is the instructive or directive (conclusion-recommendation) type. You would use it in writings that teach operation or repair and assembly. Here's how such a terminal would look if you intended to teach students how to build military housing units:

As potential members of construction crews, you should remember all the steps necessary to build an entire unit.

First, square your corners and dig footings that will support the building. Then erect foundation walls that will give the unit a sound base, next cut the floor joists, mount them so that the floor will be level, and put down the subflooring.

Cut the studs to an even 7′ 9″ and raise them at 24-inch intervals. Get them perpendicular. Then plate them so that the walls will be as square at the top as they will be at the bottom.

Make sure that your ceiling joists are evenly spaced and are nailed down with enough nails to keep them in place. Next, put on the siding, starting from the bottom and working up. Slant the nails downward so they will pull the boards together.

. . . Follow the suggestions and rules given in this manual, cut the lumber to proper lengths, drive enough nails to hold the building together, and the structure you put up will be strong enough to house military personnel safely and comfortably.

An ending like this guides the student and applies all that the material has covered. It is serviceable because it recalls the steps which students will follow once they go to work.

Which of the two types should you use? Preferably, use the one that serves your particular manuscript better. If the writing only informs, then use the first type. If the material teaches techniques or procedures, use the second. And naturally, if the material both instructs and informs, try to combine the types in the same way that you combine the material in the text.

Give the terminal a heading that functions: Highlights of Building Military Houses; The Steps in Building Military Housing Units; The Gasoline Engine Is a Functioning Machine. Use a topic that implies a synopsis and informs the reader.

WRITE THE FIRST DRAFT

Once a writer has done his research, organized his material, and prepared his outline, he is almost ready to write. But regardless of how much material he has and how well prepared he is to write a manual, a writer should find out all he can about his potential readers before he puts one word on paper. He has a plan of attack and sufficient ammunition for almost any kind of attack; but before he moves up, he should know his target. Potential readers, in this particular case, represent that target.

Find out what readers already know. You should know background facts about your potential readers. This information helps you to plan the scope and to determine the amount of technical data you may include.

When a writer knows the background of his readers he can choose the level of his material more wisely. For instance, if he knows that most of his readers have had experience in the personnel field or have studied the subject in college, he can eliminate the basic material and move into more advanced phases. But if the material he is to write will be for management or administrative trainees who have had no special training or experience, the writer would have to include fundamentals.

Learn the reading ability of your potential readers. There are several sources from which this information can be obtained. No one source by itself is adequate. You must consider all of them if you are to have the right answer.

This background information helps you to determine the readability level of the material you plan to give your readers. Table 13-1 shows the reading level of various publications, as well as their Fog Index.

TABLE 13-1

Fog Index and Reading Levels by Grade and by Magazine *

Fog Index	Reading level by grade	By magazine
17	College graduate	(No popular
16	" senior	
15	" junior	magazine
14	" sophomore	
13 Danger line	" freshman	this difficult)
12	High school senior	*Atlantic Monthly*
11	" " junior	*Harper's*
10	High school sophomore	*Time*
9	" " freshman	*Reader's Digest*
8	Eighth grade	*Ladies' Home Journal*
7	Seventh grade	*True Confessions*
6	Sixth grade	Comics

* From Robert Gunning, "The Technique of Clear Writing," McGraw-Hill Book Company, Inc., 1952.

Interest your reader; talk directly to him. If your writing is vague, general, or too scholarly, the average reader is likely to ask, "Who's this guy writing for, anyway? Me? Seems more like he's trying to impress somebody," or "It makes a lot of reading, but I don't get it."

Remember this: *It doesn't matter how well you know a subject or how thoroughly you investigate it; if your reader does not get the meaning, then you have wasted all your efforts.* He has no way of knowing what you know or how well you know it unless you transmit your facts so that he can grasp them.

Talk directly to the reader. Bring him into the discussion. Use the personal pronouns "we" and "you," but with discretion. Make him a part of the explanation just as though you were both in a room and you were describing a piece of equipment or explaining a technique. Use specific instances and simple presentations of steps; and have him seemingly take an active part in whatever is happening on the printed page.

Use the *general-to-specific* or the *specific-to-general* approach as much as you can. When you have a general rule or statement of facts to get across, do it by giving the rule and then citing specific examples to illustrate the point, or by stating examples and then explaining the general laws or procedures behind them. Ordinarily, readers find it hard to understand generalities unless specifics are applied.

Write in a lively, readable style. A lively, readable style is an arrangement of words, sentences, and paragraphs into a text that is at once appealing to the reader, informative, direct, and crystal-clear at first reading. In a piece of training literature a lively, readable style makes your reader *want* to read, find that the material applies to him, and get a clear, correct meaning from the first reading.

How do you develop a readable style?

First, no one can teach you a style; you develop it over a period of trials and errors—of writing, cutting, revising, and rewriting. But certain guides, hints, and suggestions may reduce the length of that trial-and-error period.

Use words the reader knows. First try to consider the probable vocabulary of the people who will read your material. In most cases your own vocabulary will be larger than that of your readers. And probably your writing vocabulary will include words that the readers won't know. Try to write within the bounds of a vocabulary that will not cause trouble for the reader.

Use concrete words. Use concrete words in place of abstract ones as much as possible. Words that represent visible, tangible materials usually express an idea more clearly than those which stand for invisible, intangible ideas.

Let's note here, however, that certain technical words which are difficult for the average reader have to be included in your manual. Some of them will be familiar to the readers. For instance, the word "potentiometer" is not easy, is not on any simple vocabulary list, and would wreck reading-formula counts, but many readers would understand it. Other terms, less familiar but essential to the text, must be used and explained.

Any time you introduce a new term to the reader, explain it right there—in parentheses if necessary. Where such words are essential, don't try to write around them. Just use them naturally and tell the reader what you mean. Also, if you must use electronic symbols, put them in parentheses beside the words or terms they symbolize; do this often enough so that the reader will be able to recognize the symbols when he finds them alone.

Choose action verbs. Verbs that suggest action and movement also add life to a style of writing; but verbs that indicate a state, mood, or condition do not. (See Chapter 7.)

Some writers resort to the passive voice in an attempt to keep the personal element out of a piece of writing. Here's an example:

> After a plug is unscrewed from the head, it should be cleaned in the cleaning machine and tested; then the gap should be checked before it is put back in.

Change such a sentence to read like this:

> After you *unscrew* the plugs from the head, *clean* them in the cleaning machine, *test* them, and *check* the gap before you *put* them back in.

Choose verbs that create active impressions for the reader, and steer clear of the passive voice. You thus give life to your style. If you are careful in your verb selection and use, and if you pick the concrete word instead of the abstract one, you will be taking definite steps to improve your style.

Vary your style. Vary your expressions and phrases; otherwise, particularly in a long piece, you will clog the writing with monotonous repetition. For example, a writer may be describing the various functions of a certain machine. If at each of six steps he repeats "This is what happens here," the reader becomes bored with the mechanical expression. The writer, under such circumstances, would improve the readability if he used "This is what happens here" in one place, "These changes occur here" in a second place, and so on throughout the explanation.

Take the matter of giving specific illustrations to point up a general instruction or technique; some writers mechanically repeat "for example" in every instance. You'll want to vary that device, too. Say "for example" one time, "for instance" the next, "consider the case of" next, etc. Of course, if you present many examples through the text, you cannot always find variations and you will be forced to repeat. But try not to let the repetitions come one right after another; vary them in an irregular pattern so that the reader will not be conscious of them. You can also number the examples, if the numbers will help your readers.

Certain expressions, because of overuse, have come to be meaningless; in fact, many of them are used so often in industrial and military writing that when you see the first word or two you know what comes next and are likely to skip over that part of the text. Here are some: "in accordance with," "by the authority of," "has the responsibility of," "personnel concerned will," "must be complied with," "pursuant to instructions." A writer who wants people to read what he puts on paper will do his utmost to get rid of these trite expressions.

Write effective sentences. We are not concerned here with teaching what a sentence is; technical writers should know that already. However, we are interested in certain fundamentals that help to make sentences effective.

Write shorter sentences; observe their content. Much has been said recently, in talk and in print, about the effectiveness of short sentences and the ineffectiveness of long ones. An inexperienced writer, trying to absorb all this, may come up with a distorted view: he may conclude that short sentences *alone* will make his writing easier to read.

True, short sentences are generally effective; but they do not achieve effectiveness simply by being short. Length and content work together. In other words, a sentence with 15 words is not valuable because it has only 15 words; it is valuable to the text—note that, *to the text*—because of what it says and how it says it. Look at this example:

The expansion was implemented by two rods working against each other, pulling from the center.

It has 15 words in it and by syllabic count it does not fall into the difficult-reading category; yet almost any critic would say that it is not a very effective sentence. Why?

For one thing, an abstract word holds the key idea; for another, the main verb is in the passive voice and is "inactive"; and finally, the sentence depends on two *-ing* verbs to convey the real action. Let's improve the sentence:

Two rods pull from the center and work against each other to help expand the [whatever is being expanded].

Again we used 15 words; also, we have kept the original meaning. But now the sentence uses active verbs that replace the *-ing* words; the *-ion* word has yielded to a basic verb form; and the sequence of events is in logical order.

Suppose we explore the point a bit further. Here is a paragraph, taken from a training project, in which the writer has conscientiously kept down sentence length:

Clear vision is necessary in flying military aircraft; therefore, proper maintenance of transparent enclosures is of primary importance. Every effort should be made to avoid scratching or finger-printing transparent enclosures while servicing. Plastics are much softer than glass and scratch easily. This reduces visibility which is extremely fatiguing to flying personnel. [*Is visibility fatiguing? Are scratches?*] A dry rag should never be used for cleaning as the surface will be scratched by the dust being removed. The surface should be cleaned by washing with plenty of mild soap and cold water, using a clean, soft, grit-free cloth, sponge, or bare hands. It should then be dried with a chamois or soft cloth taking care not to rub after the plastic is dry. If oil or grease is present, kerosene may be used. Gasoline, acetone, benzene, or lacquer thinners are never used for this purpose as they will "craze" the surface.

The longest sentence has only 26 words, and all the others have less than 20. So if short sentences make effective reading, this paragraph should fall into that category.

But it is not effective, and any reader knows it. The writer has the thoughts and ideas; but he does not use direct, active sentences. Although he has kept the sentences short, he makes the material impersonal and approaches his presentation from an inactive viewpoint. Suppose we rewrite the material to make the sentences effective.

Flying personnel need to see clearly out of military aircraft; therefore, we must give transparent enclosures proper maintenance. These enclosures, made of plastic, scratch easily because they are much softer than glass. Since scratches reduce visibility, and reduced visibility fatigues flying personnel, maintenance people must try not to scratch or fingerprint these enclosures while servicing them. To clean the surfaces, you should wash them with plenty of mild soap and cold water, using a clean, soft rag, and sponge, or your bare hands. *Don't use a dry rag that will pick up dust particles and scratch the surface.* When you have washed the surface, dry it carefully with a chamois or soft cloth, taking care not to rub after the plastic is dry. *Caution:* If you find oil or grease on the surface, clean it with kerosene only. Don't use gasoline, acetone, benzene, or lacquer thinners because these will "craze" the surface.

The sentences here become effective not so much because of their length as because of their activeness and directness.

As a rule, short sentences inform the reader and appeal to him more effectively than long ones when both have the same tone, the same word choice, and the same directness or indirectness.

Steer clear of inversions. Among other things, they lead to over-punctuated sentence structures. Look at these examples of inversion:

Some pilots, even the best ones, can make mistakes.

One does not think, perhaps, that students are critical of what they read.

A periscope trainer should, under these conditions, be sent to a repair shop.

The fault with TP's, some people think, is in their appearance.

Now let's improve them:

Even the best pilots can make mistakes.

Perhaps one does not think that students are critical readers.

Under these conditions a periscope trainer should be sent to the repair shop.

Some people think the fault with the TP's is in their appearance.

Notice how much more smoothly the improved sentences flow. Of course you cannot always eliminate inversions without changing the meaning of the sentence; often you will actually need them for continuity. But try to avoid those which have no purpose.

Cut down the number of parenthetical expressions. These, like inversions, interrupt the flow of sentences. In some instances you cannot get rid of them. But if you can recast the sentences effectively so that the modifiers do not have to be punctuated, by all means recast them. Note these examples:

The generator, which is mounted to get power from the fan belt, creates current to charge the battery.

These skis, hollow and made of waterproof plywood, must be inspected frequently.

That seaman, the one who was just in this office, was a professional dancer before he came into service.

Change them to read this way:

The generator creates current to charge the battery; it is mounted so that it can get power from the fan belt.

The skis are hollow and are made of waterproof plywood. You must inspect them frequently.

That seaman who was just in this office was a professional dancer before he came into service.

Go easy with short, choppy sentences. Occasionally used, they add emphasis, but if used too frequently, they result in a primerlike style.

Be cautious with fragments. Like choppy sentences, sentence fragments may be very useful and effective in a piece of writing *if* the writer recognizes them and handles them skillfully. Noun, adjective, and adverbial clauses become sentence fragments when treated as sentences (begun with a capital letter and ended with period). A writer should be sure he knows when a fragment is a fragment before trying to use one for emphasis. You've seen fragments that you know the writers did not recognize; they looked like the examples below and they left you clutching the atmosphere for meanings:

When there is no other course to follow.

That which you were told to do.

When fitted into the escape hatch panel.

As the orders stated.

The part of the wing that joins the fuselage.

Not one of these could be called an effective fragment out of context; probably not one could be effective, even in the manuscript. Generally, you would do well to avoid fragments until you have enough experience to know when one would be useful to emphasize a point. The following paragraph has a useful fragment:

Of course this doesn't mean that every time you run out of fuel-line tubing you can run down to a handy parts shop and buy what you want. *Nor go to the base exchange for it.* But where such parts are needed to keep cars and trucks rolling, and where normal supply channels could cause maintenance delay, by all means buy locally.

This fragment gets independent treatment for emphasis. Notice that its meaning ties in with the preceding sentence; the fragment is not used to express an independent thought but is, in a sense, an afterthought. In most cases an effective fragment follows and adds to a preceding sentence. Faulty ones—and most of those that you read fall into this category—usually do not follow; they lead.

The best thing to do about fragments is to avoid them; but if you do use them, make sure they come as a second thought to modify and emphasize the main idea. And be sure, too, when you use them that *the reader knows you know what you're doing.*

Personalize; get the reader into the act. While we are talking about the make-up of sentences, we should bring in one other related matter —the personal style of writing for reader-participation. Earlier we mentioned using the personal pronouns; but now let's see when they should and should not be used.

Preferably, a writer leaves *I* out of training material because it iden-fies him too closely with the writing; this identification often gives an opinionated slant to an otherwise objective presentation. However he should use *we* and *you* properly to get the reader into the act.

Use the *we* to suggest a cooperative venture: you and the readers are doing something together. But do not use it when it has the implication of the *editorial we* behind it. What's the difference? Here are some sentences in which *we* (or *us*) is used properly:

We should observe this action before studying all the phases. [The writer and the readers are observing.]
It is necessary for us first to consider the engine now in use. [The readers *and* the writer consider the engine.] We have seen how the distributor sends current to the right place at the right time. [The writer *and* readers have seen the action.]

The use of *you,* the other personal pronoun that leads to reader-participation, probably needs more study than the use of *we.* This is true because many writers tend to depend on *you* too much in their efforts to reach the reader. In fact, the *you*-viewpoint is so over-done in some writing that the resulting manuscripts are monotonously "you-y."

To make *you* fit naturally into a style and become a useful device in the writing, this list of check points may help:

1. Use *you*'s normally, as you would in classroom teaching.

You probably noticed that we have omitted from this study any reference to frequency modulation.

2. Use fewer *you*'s in writing than in conversation.

If you forget to make entries in your report, your ground maintenance people may not give you the service you need. [In writing, this sentence would be less obvious if written like this: If you forget to make entries in the report, ground maintenance people may not give the needed service.]

3. Put *you*'s into introductions, transitions, and summaries when they fit naturally.

You've seen people who know a lot of theories but do not know how to put those theories into practice. That's why this manual is planned as it is; when you finish the study, you should know what the theories are and how they work. In other words, you'll be able to put principles into practice.

What do these evaluation steps mean to you? They mean that you have a specific way of knowing what your students have done in the past and are doing at the present time. With this information you can make reasonable predictions as to what they should be able to do at the end of the training period.

4. Put *you*'s into interpretations, analogies, and specific examples.

You can compare the way a rod works on a crankshaft to the way a man's foot and leg work on a bicycle pedal.

5. Use *you*'s when explaining techniques, procedures, and practices.

First, you should take a lint-free rag and wipe away all dust particles. Then, using a ¼″ brush, coat the entire surface with a thin layer of solvent. You can wipe this away within five minutes if you're in a hurry; but you can get best results if you leave the cleaner on the surface for 30 minutes to an hour.

6. Try to imply *you* more often and don't depend on its actual presence in the sentence.

Remember to follow this 1–2–3 procedure; remove the plugs one at a time, being careful to keep them lined up according to the cylinders from which they came and carefully clean away all traces of carbon and unburned fuels; set the gaps; and then test each plug before you replace it.

7. Avoid *you*'s that appear obvious when you have a series within a sentence.

Before beginning to work on an engine, check your tool kit for wrenches, pliers, three screwdrivers, hammer, and compression meter.

8. Avoid *you*'s when you're explaining a policy or a principle.

When a spark ignites the fuel-air mixture inside the cylinder, the expanding gases push the piston down.

(The sentence would appear awkward if it ran this way:

When your spark ignites your fuel-air mixture, the expanding gases push your piston down.)

9. Avoid *you*'s that change a sentence from an objective statement to an opinion.

Technical orders cover almost every technical practice or procedure which Navy mechanics follow. NOT: You'll come to think that technical orders cover almost every practice or procedure which Navy mechanics follow.

10. Avoid *you*'s when you're describing a piece of equipment.

A freely or universally mounted gyroscope is free to rotate in any direction about its center of gravity.

11. Generally, avoid *you*'s in a review of history.

The history of our present Air Force had an insignificant beginning: In 1907 a Signal Corps officer and two enlisted men were assigned to take care of all aircraft and related equipment.

12. Avoid *you*'s when you're writing about industrial and military matters that must have objective treatment.

The acrobatic maneuvers you will learn to perform are the loop, barrel, roll, Immelmann, slow roll, and the half roll and reverse. *All of these maneuvers will be performed with the following power settings and flight conditions: gyros caged, throttle at 25″ Hg.*

CHOOSE THE ILLUSTRATIONS

Since material written to teach or inform usually needs illustrations to support the text, it becomes part of the author's job to suggest the illustrations in the manuscript. However you should not wait until you complete the first draft to think about graphs, schematics, and drawings which readers will need. If you wait until after the writing is finished and the material has become "cold" you may not include all the illustrations necessary to make the text clear.

How can we go about relating text and illustrations in the best fashion? We can: pick the passages to be illustrated, choose the most appropriate illustrations, integrate illustrations and text, prepare illustrations properly, use color if it is absolutely necessary, work with the illustrator.

Pick the passages to be illustrated. Pick the text passages that you want illustrated *while you are writing*; don't wait until you have done all the writing to go back through the manuscript, slapping in pictures here and there.

Also, don't rely on memory when you pick passages. In other words, don't just say to yourself, "I think a cutaway of . . . fits here," and expect to remember that thought six or seven weeks later.

Choose illustrations for your particular text. When you pick a place that needs illustrating, choose the kind of illustration you want *right then.* Don't "wait until later," and then wind up not knowing what you do want. Go ahead and choose it: (1) give a specific reference showing where to find it; (2) cut it out of a magazine, book or manual; (3) sketch it in detail; (4) tell what photograph you'll need; or, if nothing else, (5) write a detailed word picture so the illustrator can draw what you want.

As you know, some illustrations help to teach a certain technique or procedure, some point up a pertinent idea or thought, and others summarize or identify information. For example, a wiring diagram, properly labeled, helps to teach a radio student how to repair equipment. An illustration of an industrial or military form may just show what the form looks like, or it may show how to use the form. (NOTE: If you are merely identifying the form, your explanation will run one way; if you are explaining how to use it, your explanation will be slanted differently.) And a picture of a man sitting in the cockpit of an airplane with his hands on the controls may show *how to sit, what to do with the hands,* or *which knobs to hold.*

Select the illustration to fit the specific purpose of the text it supports and to fit the actual needs of the reader.

If you're writing an orientation book for new pilots, and you want them to identify the instruments, an illustration of the instruments will be better than a cutaway. But if you're writing a book for instrument repairmen, you'll help the reader more if you use a well-labeled cutaway that shows how the working parts fit together.

What kinds of illustrations can you use?

Here are a few types—photographs, line drawings, schematics and wiring diagrams, operating and maintenance forms, charts and graphs, maps, renderings, cartoons, etc.

The process used to print your work has a lot to do with the type of illustrations you use. For instance, if reproduction is to be done by mimeograph, you are limited to simple black-and-white line drawings.

When reproduction is accomplished by large printing plants, you may use any of the other types of illustrations if the specs allow them. Be sure to know which facility you intend to use before planning the illustrations.

Integrate illustrations and text. Once you've decided on the illustrations, you must integrate them with the text. You can do this by: (1) putting illustrations near the text they support, (2) making timely and adequate references to the illustrations, (3) discussing them in detail in your writing.

Put illustrations near supported text: A writer should put his illustrations as close as possible to the text they support. Specifically, he should put them in as soon as he can after he has made the first reference. Why?

Because he confuses the reader if he tells him to look at a picture, then makes him read through or skip over several paragraphs to get to it. When a student gets directions to look at something, he tends to look then; if he doesn't find it close to the reference, he may feel that he should read on a while longer before looking.

When you put an illustration into the text, indicate on the manuscript just where you want it to go. A good idea is to draw a block on the manuscript page and type directions in it. What you say within the block will depend on each individual illustration. But say enough for the preparing agencies to know what the illustration will mean.

Refer to illustrations: Placement alone, however, does not guarantee that a reader will look at the illustration. Definitely refer to it
in the copy at the exact time that you want him to look. Your wording should be so clear that it almost says to the reader: "Look at the
picture of . . . right now."

Perhaps the best way to explain how to refer to illustrations is to
consider these sentences:

As you see in the wiring diagram of the S-31 set, the leads are. . . .

Note that the left hand holds the throttle control, as the illustration
"The Proper Position in the Cockpit" indicates, and the right hand. . . .

Now look at the picture of the mechanic tightening the head bolts; notice that he has a. . . .

Run the wire from the primary coil, as wiring diagram shows, beneath
the. . . .

References like these serve a double purpose; they make an informative statement and they lead the reader to the illustration.

In some instances you may have to refer to illustrations by placement: "above," "below," "to the right," "to the left," "on the following page." If so, be sure to make the reference right there in the
text. The directions you give may have to be changed when the
layout people put copy and illustrations together. But if you don't
make a definite statement and thus allow room for proper directions
later, the layout man has trouble making room for a whole sentence.

Discuss illustrations in text: When you put an illustration into
a manual or pamphlet, use it; talk about it in the text so that it
actually helps the reader. Tell him to notice this and that and the
other; point out how several parts of the illustration make the writing
more meaningful. Don't expect that a single reference will make the
reader see everything you want him to.

Illustrations used in training publications have a specific purpose:
to help the reader understand the text. But if the writer fails to tie
his pictures to the descriptions and explanations, he not only fails
to help the reader but may actually confuse him.

If you have a long section of writing that depends on an illustration, make frequent references to the illustration: talk about the

parts and what they mean; discuss the workings; explain the assembly. Whatever you do, use the illustration to support the text; and use the text to support the illustration. Don't make just one or two tie-ins and expect the reader to get everything from labels alone. Remember, then, to: (1) put the illustrations near the text, (2) refer to them so the reader will know when to look, and (3) discuss them so that they become integral parts of the text.

How to prepare illustrations: Once you decide to use a certain illustration, prepare it so that it will serve a definite purpose. To prepare an illustration, you should: (1) label all necessary parts, (2) give the illustration a good talking caption, and (3) decide how large the reproduced illustration should be.

Work with the illustrator: There are a few authors who can draw as well as they can write, but only a few. In most instances writers depend on artists to draw suitable illustrations for the manual. Frequently writers have to ask artists to retouch photographs so that the illustrations can really supplement the text.

But this does not mean that the writers only write and that they leave the illustrating to the artist. Though the artist knows his own job, ordinarily he does not know the text as well as the author does.

Obviously, then, writers and illustrators must pool their efforts to make a manual or pamphlet really effective. In other words, writers get the ideas and pass them on to the artist. The artist, in turn, draws the illustration to fit the need as the author has explained it.

When to use color with illustrations. In some cases you may want to add color to the illustration. Frequently color makes an illustration more effective than black and white. However, you shouldn't throw reds, blues, and greens into a diagram, chart, or photograph just because you think it's prettier that way.

Because of the cost, time, and trouble involved, you should not use extra colors unless they are actually necessary. In other words, use colors only when they help the reader understand the illustration. If blue, red, or yellow lines emphasize parts of a management chart, and if the illustration would be vague or confusing without the colors, then you are justified in using them. Or if a switch is blue or green on a particular piece of equipment and should be treated realistically in the illustration, than color should be used.

Generally, though, try not to use extra colors if you don't absolutely need them. And be sure to check the specs to see if they allow color. The budget or the printing facilities may make it impossible.

POLISH YOUR TEXT

The first draft of the manuscript, of course, is important. In it the writer has presented his subject matter in a logical sequence so that it is a single unit. Also, he has tried to make his text clear, direct, and easy to read.

But no first draft should stand as the final copy. Regardless of how much effort has gone into its making, the first draft practically always needs to be edited and revised.

When you have a complete first draft of a manuscript, you must then consider it in the light of what the final product should be. This is true whether you are editing your own or someone else's manuscript. The first step of such consideration is to appraise the text for over-all content and approach.

Appraise for content and approach. A manuscript for a training manual should fill a particular need. The author knew the objectives and purpose demanded before he ever started to write; he investigated those factors during the research stage. But now that he has a first draft, he must see whether the written material fills the bill.

The big question is this: Does the material do what it is intended to do? Or does it just present a lot of information? In other words, does the manual show what to do? How to do it? When? What actions to take under what circumstances?

If you feel that your manuscript completely covers the topics and does a good job of explaining techniques, practices, and procedures, check it with the technical specialists who helped you. Send copies of the manuscript to all those who gave you information and ask them to check the technical aspects of the material. Specifically, ask them to check for technical accuracy, for completeness of coverage, and for clarity. Also ask them to check the material in the light of operating needs. Regardless of the manuscript's plan and content, it must help its readers do a better job. No matter how accurate and complete the theoretical information, if the writer has not applied that information to specific needs—needs of using firms or agencies and needs of readers—then the material will fall short.

Only when the technicians have given you the go-ahead signal are you ready to begin revising and reworking the manuscript. First, rework its organization, if necessary. Second, edit it for accuracy, clarity, coherence, and mechanical and grammatical correctness.

Reorganize and rework the manuscript. Read the manuscript straight through, just as if you were a critical reviewer. As you go through the text, study the way you have treated each topic. Also, pay attention to the sequence of ideas. And check particularly any passages that seem repetitious. As you read, ask yourself such questions as these:

a. Are the various parts in the best possible order?

b. Does this section in Chapter 5 fit well where it is? Or would it be more appropriate in Chapter 8?

c. Should this heading be subdivided and given fuller treatment? Or should it be reduced and made subordinate to another topic?

d. Didn't I say this (you're reading Chapter 6) back in Chapter 4? If so, should I cut it out in one place? Or should I combine the two discussions?

e. I've handled this as a subtopic, but I've given it a detailed treatment. Should I cut some of the details? Or make it a major section?

f. Do I need this material at all? Couldn't I cut it without harming the text?

g. By making this section a separate one, am I emphasizing it too much?

h. Should I rearrange these chapters and make Chapter 4 the third one?

Makes notes in the margin of the manuscript as you read. But don't try to reorganize until you have read the entire text. Otherwise you may lose perspective and get a distorted view of the entire work.

After you've reviewed the manuscript, go back over the notes you've made and evaluate them. Where you've suggested deletions, block out the sections and see if the material reads better. Where you've noted shifts of passages from one place in the manuscript to another, move the material around and read the new arrangement.

Remember this: Read and criticize your manuscript objectively. Then compare the original conceptions to the criticisms. Adjust the two, and the final product will be more useful.

After you have reworked and reorganized the manuscript, the next step is to edit it.

Edit what you have written. When you begin to edit, start with big areas first and work down: check for accuracy of technical passages; delete all unnecessary material—words, paragraphs, or sections of information; appraise the paragraphs and rearrange them for unity and continuity if necessary; make sure that transitions bridge gaps, that terminals synopsize the material they terminate, and that headings apply to the text; enliven dry or dull passages; and finally, correct punctuation and spelling.

Have accurate material. While reading your manuscript, imagine that you are an editor. An editor critically appraises the ideas that are expressed. For example, when he reads statements that represent facts, he determines from his own knowledge or from bibliographical sources whether or not the statements are true; if quoted, whether or not they are exact. If the passages represent condensations or paraphrases he makes sure that the writer did not slant or distort the original meaning. If the writer has drawn specific conclusions, the editor tests their soundness; specifically, he looks for conclusions drawn from insufficient data, for false analogies, for biased opinions, for emotional weighting, for editorialized expressions or implications, and for vague generalities.

Let's examine these faults.

Sometimes a writer tends to *draw conclusions from insufficient data*; he fails to investigate all angles of a particular question. For example, he may read that one B-52 can do the work of three B-29's. So, instead of weighing all the facts—relative costs, required flying conditions, types of targets, etc.—he uses this statement as a basis for a particular conclusion. Or he may find that under certain conditions one type of generator will last longer than another and, without regard for other factors, state that this particular generator is the most reliable one.

Again, a writer may believe or "feel" that a certain idea is true. He is using insufficient data if he makes a great effort to support his theory with arguments from many sources and cites in support of the opposing idea only those few sources which are easily available and obvious. This type of reasoning, sometimes called "stacking the evidence," is, whatever you call it, another example of drawing conclusions from incomplete data.

Another type of faulty reasoning that an editor is on the watch for is the *false analogy*. A writer uses false analogy when he says that because one fact or characteristic with regard to two subjects is true, all others are true or are in proportion.

An average man is roughly 5 times as tall as the average cat is long. Since a cat can jump a distance equal to six times its length, a man can jump a distance equal to 30 times his height.

A man jumps 170 feet? Only off a bridge, and only at the risk of his life.

Not all analogies are bad, however; many of them are quite good, and most of the good ones help to explain otherwise difficult facts. One like this would be acceptable:

A connecting rod acts on a crankshaft in a manner similar to that of a man's foot and ankle on a bicycle pedal.

The thought to remember is this: If you use analogies, be sure they fit the text, that they are sound, and that they are applicable. The ones to look for and to cut whenever you find them are the bad ones that give false support to an idea.

Biased opinions instead of objective results constitute a third type of poor reasoning in a manuscript. Biased opinions may get into a manuscript as a result of lack of evidence to support a particular point.

Often the reader is led to believe he is getting an established fact and he accepts it as such because of the wording of the opinions. Here is an example of this type of opinion:

Sixty students received class instruction but no laboratory work, while another 60 were given laboratory work but no classroom explanations. Then all 120 took the same examination. Fifty-six of those who had laboratory time passed the test, but only 42 of the other group passed. *Nevertheless, classroom time should be given preference because of ease of handling and low cost.*

The last sentence presumes to be a rational, factual conclusion; but it does not stem from the preceding data. Where are the figures on cost and ease of handling? If the conclusion is really true, the writer should present supporting evidence.

Of course, in some cases writers cannot get sufficient data because of new equipment or unavailable experimental results; they may be forced to draw some conclusion that is purely an opinion. If so, they should clearly label the thought as an opinion. Try this substitute for the last sentence of the example just given.

Nevertheless, until more tests have been run, *we believe it wiser* to continue operating classes as they have been run in the past because of ease of handling and economy.

Notice the difference? If you must use an opinion, tag it; don't lead the reader to believe he is getting facts when he is not.

Some writers resort to *emotional weighting* when they present ideas in a piece of writing. This type of false or misleading presentation usually takes the form of adjectives and adverbs injected to suggest undue value (or lack of it), as in these examples:

This *startling* discovery means that a new machine will be in production soon.

You *simply* remove the rubber line and replace it with a copper one. [If you have to replace hydraulic lines fastened inside the wing of a B-52, the operation is not a simple one.]

The experiment had *dire* results. [Did it? Or did it just fail?]

The next step, the *hardest*, is to clean the carbon from the piston head.

No doubt you have seen many sentences like these in training literature. In most cases the loaded words could be removed without affecting the sentence meaning.

Editorializing, another device to look for and eliminate in your writing, means that the writer puts a comment, a criticism, or an analysis into a factual passage. Again, as with biased opinions instead of objective results, editorial statements are often subtly woven into the text in such a way that they do not stand out to a casual reader; and often they taint a paragraph or section until it is out of line with facts or logic. Perhaps you have seen editorial remarks like the italicized sentence in this passage:

Airplane builders use three types of washers in aircraft structures: plain washers, lock washers, and special washers. *Lock washers are obviously the best of the three types.* They are used with machine screws or bolts, whenever the self-locking or castellated type nut is not applicable.

Factual statements before and after the editorial remark give it an appearance of fact when in reality it expresses an opinion. Of course, the lock washer *may be* the best of the three; but this is an explanatory section, not an analytical one. So the sentence should be deleted.

The final fallacy, the *vague generality*, turns up as a broad, sweeping statement that does little more than fill space; and almost always a generality leaves questions in the minds of the readers:

Graduates of this school write and ask for copies of this guide all the time. [All graduates? Just a few? Specifically, how many? Why? All the time—24 hours a day?]

Pilots prefer this type of parachute. [Do they? Based on survey? Or guesswork? Did they say so? Prefer it to what?]

Most mechanics receive promotions soon after they finish this course. [What are the percentages? How long after they finish?]

A simple suggestion with regard to vague generalities is this: delete them. If you have an idea in a generality that seems to be essential, then make something of it! Don't leave the vagueness in. Take the examples we just listed; they could be corrected to read:

Every week since last January we have received at least six requests for this manual from graduates now assigned as photographers.

Seven out of 10 pilots say they prefer the chest parachute to the cushion type.

Seventy-five per cent of the mechanics who have taken this course during the last year have been promoted at least one grade; and 10 per cent have been upgraded twice.

Sentences like these transmit meaningful ideas to the reader; but sentences like the earlier versions do not. Remember the differences when you do your original writing or edit a first draft.

Make sure the manuscript is a clear, coherent unit. Another aspect of this editing process is to check the unity, clarity, and interest of the material. Keep these questions before you during the second review:

a. Do the paragraphs form such a continuous whole that a reader will not be confused by a single one of them?

b. Do all the paragraphs fit where they are?

c. Could one part or section be taken from its present place and put in another one to make the explanation clear?

d. Does a reader know when the writer has finished a given explanation?

e. Does the reader know when he is moving from one topic to another?

f. Finally, does this passage or that one seem too dull and dry?

An editor—either the original author or another person—should think of himself during this second reading as a reader picking up the manuscript for the first time. If the manuscript leads him along a clear line of reasoning, if it interests him and holds his attention during the process, then the writer has presented his subject in satisfactory fashion. But if he has to glance back over earlier sections to know where he is, then the material needs rearranging and additional road signs—topic sentences, transitions, and terminals.

Evaluate the manuscript's readability. Formulas help much more *after* the writing than *during* its course. Only when you believe the manuscript satisfies most of the demands of a readable style and personal interest should you turn to formulas. You can use the Flesch Scale of readability, the Fog count, or any of the many other formulas.

Let's realize right now that formulas alone will not make dull writing interesting. Formulas used properly as measuring devices are valuable; no one will deny that. But if handled as guides during the time of writing, they become tools incorrectly used. They will not substitute for clear thinking, and they will not keep a writer from having to apply the suggestions given in this chapter.

Check mechanics and grammar. The final editing step gets down to the fundamentals of writing—grammar and punctuation. Regardless of how experienced he is, no editor or writer should omit this part of his work. Material that is to teach or inform should be well handled mechanically and grammatically.

SEND THE TEXT AND ILLUSTRATIONS TO PRODUCTION

Don't waste time once your manual is finished. Get it into production immediately. Work closely with the art and production departments. Then you will be certain to obtain a manual that is a credit to yourself and your associates.

When deciding on format, binding, and paper quality, follow the specifications and recommendations of your art and production departments. Only then can you be sure of good results.

Note that while we've confined our attention to training manuals in this chapter the methods can be used with any other type of manual. Thus, many of the above suggestions are usable with instruction manuals, catalogs, bulletins, etc.

SUMMARY

The six steps in writing any training manual are: organize your material, plan a coherent whole, write the first draft, chose the illustrations, polish the text, and send the copy and illustrations to the production department. By using this approach to the job of writing a manual you will produce a better manuscript in less time.

CHAPTER CHECK-UP

1. Give the six essential steps in writing a training manual.
2. Can these steps be used for other types of manuals? Explain.
3. What three steps should you take in choosing a preliminary content for your manual?
4. What makes a good working title? Explain. Give three examples of good titles.
5. How can you make a preliminary topic list? Where can you get topic ideas?
6. Can conferences give you needed information? How?
7. What kinds of published materials are valuable for research? How can you keep track of facts and sources?
8. Describe how you would prepare an outline.
9. Choose a topic for a training manual and prepare a complete outline for the manual. Assume that the manual will have 200 published pages and will have about 20 main headings and 125 subheadings.
10. What kinds of topic entries can you use in an outline? Give examples of each.
11. What is a main-heading outline? How can you use it to save time?
12. What methods can you use to present material to your readers? Give one example of each method.
13. How can you make your manual a coherent unit?
14. Why is a good lead important? Give three examples of good leads.
15. What are relationship-showing devices? How can you use them?

16. Give an example of comparisons; of contrast; of the exception to a rule.
17. Define a paragraph. Why must a paragraph be carefully constructed?
18. Give four guides for holding the reader's attention. Explain each.
19. Why should you introduce new ideas with a topic sentence?
20. How can you mark the end of thoughts? Give two examples.
21. What is an effective terminal? Give an example of three effective terminal sections from training manuals.
22. How can you determine how much your readers already know?
23. Give the typical reading level of various publications. How can these reading levels guide you in your writing?
24. How can you talk directly to your reader? Give three examples.
25. What is a lively, readable style? How can you develop one?
26. Why is it important that you choose words your readers know? Give examples of good and poor words.
27. Why are concrete words important? Give five examples of concrete words.
28. What is an action verb? Why should you use action verbs? Give six examples of action verbs.
29. Why should you vary your style? What does the reader gain? Cite two ways of varying the style of your manual.
30. How can you write more effective sentences? Give five examples of poor and good sentences.
31. How can you personalize your writing? Give three examples of how you can get your reader into the act.
32. Give six ways of relating illustrations to the text of your manual.
33. Where can you obtain illustrations?
34. What kinds of illustrations can you use in training manuals?
35. List and discuss three ways of integrating illustrations and text.
36. How should you prepare illustrations so that your readers will get the most from them?
37. What must a caption do to be effective? Give three examples of effective captions.
38. Why is it important that you know how big the published illustration will be?
39. How can you work with the illustrator? Why is cooperation important?
40. When should you consider color for illustrations? Why is it important that you check the specs before making the final decision in using color?
41. How can you appraise your manuscript for content and approach?

42. How can you reorganize and rework your manuscript?
43. Why is it important that you edit what you've written? What should you look for when you edit?
44. Why is complete, accurate material important?
45. How can you be sure your manuscript is a coherent unit?
46. Give two ways of evaluating readability.
47. What should you keep in mind about readability formulas? Should you use a formula while writing, or after writing? Why?
48. What should you do as soon as the text and illustrations are finished? Who and what will help you fix format, binding, and paper quality?

Chapter 14

HOW TO WRITE BETTER INDUSTRIAL CATALOGS AND ADVERTISING

If you do much technical writing you're almost certain to run into industrial catalog and advertising jobs.[1] Many of these will come to you by indirect routes. For instance, the sales department may find one of its catalogs doesn't give enough information. So the manager comes to you for more data. Within minutes you're telling the sales manager how the catalog should be written. Or worse yet, you're rewriting a paragraph for him.

With ads the approach is often different. You are asked to check an ad. Just the technical content, you know. Technically the ad is correct. But from the writing angle it's for nuclear scientists—instead of the auto mechanics who'll be reading it. So you get out a pencil and begin making suggestions. From then on, every important ad the company publishes will wind up on your desk just before press time.

Writing catalogs, bulletins, and ads is a challenging task worthy of your writing skills. And this phase of technical writing can be lucrative—if you're good. Let's take a quick look at how catalogs and ads differ from other kinds of technical writing. We'll look at catalogs first.

---

[1] See Julian Boone, ed., "Industrial Advertising Handbook," McGraw-Hill Book Company, Inc., New York, 1953, for a comprehensive discussion of all phases of industrial advertising.

216

CATALOGS SHOULD INFORM USERS AND MOTIVATE SALES

To paraphrase a well-known catalog collection: *Buyers seeking sellers use catalogs; sellers seeking buyers use advertising.* Keep these two principles in mind and you'll write better industrial copy with far less pain.

Catalogs are used by many potential buyers. Every time a man reaches for a catalog a sale hangs in the balance. If the catalog contains the information he wants, there's a good chance the sale will be made. If the catalog doesn't have the data, you're lost. For busy engineers and scientists want a quick answer. The catalog must give enough data for the reader to decide if he wants to know more about your product. A skimpy, poorly prepared catalog implies an inferior product.

WHAT IS A CATALOG?

The simplest answer is that a catalog is a basic source of information about products. It must tell the user what you have for sale. And it must help the user to decide if your product can help him. Anson A. MacLaren[2] defines a catalog as *a form of advertising which wraps up in a single package the full details about a product or group of products to give information quickly and easily so a salesman need not be called until an order is to be placed.*

Users refer to a catalog to get answers to basic questions *before* the salesman is called. So you must write your catalog to give a user the answers he wants. How can you do this? It isn't easy but it can be done.

PLAN YOUR CATALOG BEFORE YOU WRITE

To write effective sales-getting catalogs you must:

1. Decide the purpose of the catalog.
2. Determine who will use it.
3. Decide what information to include.
4. Choose the best way to present data.

Let's see how we can apply these methods to your catalogs.

[2] *Ibid.*, p. 186.

Decide the purpose. Why is this catalog being written? Ask yourself this question before you put a word on paper. Is this to be (*a*) a mail-order catalog, (*b*) a single-product catalog, (*c*) a distributor's or jobber's catalog, (*d*) a condensed catalog, or (*e*) a prefiled catalog? The answers to these questions will tell you the purpose of your catalog.

Most technical writers in industry today are called on to write the single-product catalog, condensed catalog, or prefiled catalog. So we'll give these the most attention.

Determine the users. A catalog for an auto mechanic has a much different approach from one for a research scientist. Unless you know exactly who your readers will be you can't decide what approach to use. So investigate your readers. What is their average education? Do they read regularly? What is their favorite reading matter? What do they want from a catalog? Prices? Design data? Dimensions? Weights? Only when you know the answers to these questions can you plan an effective catalog that will help sell your product.

What information should I include? This ties back to your reader and his needs. Make a list of these needs. Then include answers to as many of these needs as you can. Don't overlook items like finish, color, materials, sizes, capacities, allowable loadings, speed, range, fuel consumption, models available, discounts, dealers' addresses, phone numbers, etc.

Choose the best way to present data. What is your reader accustomed to using? Charts? Tables? Circuit diagrams? Include those he is familiar with. For he'll find your catalog easier to use and more helpful.

Remember—the catalog indirectly reflects your company and its products. Write a serviceable catalog and the users will buy your product. Don't use extravagant colors, complicated foldouts, or cheap emotional appeals. If your reader wants these he won't turn to a catalog. He'll buy a publication that provides these better than any catalog ever could. Catalogs are not designed for leisure reading—they're tools, just like a hammer or saw.

WRITING THE CATALOG

There are six steps in writing effective catalogs: (1) Collect your data and illustrations. (2) Make an outline. (3) Write a rough draft.

(4) Check your facts. (5) Polish the rough draft. (6) Send copy and art to the production department.

Data and illustrations. Get these from the engineering, sales, and advertising departments. Try to get the latest data and illustrations. For if you get old ones now you'll have to change them before the catalog is published. This leads to wasted effort, lost time, and mis-understandings. And don't overlook customers as potential sources of illustrations. Many of your customers will be glad to supply photos of your product in use. Or they'll allow you to visit their plant to take photos of your product in use.

Don't cut costs on illustrations. Get the best. Remember—you're after sales. The better the appearance of your catalog, the greater your chances of making the important sale.

Insist on being supplied *all* data related to the product. True, you may use only a tenth of it. But having the data on hand will help you write your text. This will show up in the greater assurance your writing reflects.

Make an outline. You'll be lost without one. Study other catalogs to see how they're written. And don't overlook your competitors! Some of your best ideas may result from reading poorly executed catalogs. (Not your own, of course.)

Here is the outline of a well-prepared 12-page catalog on valves for high-pressure steam. Note the sequence of the various items:

Yarway Welbond Valves for High Pressures and Temperatures

1. Front cover (1 page)
    a. Title of catalog
    b. Three photos of valve
    c. Catalog table of contents
    d. Company name; address of home office; telephone number
    e. Catalog number; date of issue
2. Valve details (2 pages)
    a. Materials
    b. Packing
    c. Handwheels
    d. Seat, disk
    e. Body, yoke, nozzle
    f. Valve uses (over 12 listed and described)

        g. Special valve features—materials, seat, stem, packing, accessible parts

3. Valve selection (2 pages)
   - *a.* Range of pressure and sizes
   - *b.* Dimensions and weights
   - *c.* Prices
   - *d.* Installation and maintenance notes
   - *e.* How to select proper valves
   - *f.* Selection table
   - *g.* Pressure rating chart

4. Typical installations (2 pages)
   - *a.* Ten photos of typical installations, with captions
   - *b.* List of 37 representative users of these valves

5. Valves for 1500 psi (1 page)
   - *a.* Cross-section drawing
   - *b.* Parts and materials list
   - *c.* Text on typical uses, ways to order
   - *d.* Dimension drawings (2 views)
   - *e.* Tabulation of valve figure number, dimensions, weights, stem rise

6. Valves for 2500 psi (1 page)
   - *a.* Cross-section drawing
   - *b.* Parts and materials list
   - *c.* Text on typical uses, ways to order
   - *d.* Dimension drawings (2 views)
   - *e.* Tabulation of valve figure number, dimensions, weights, stem rise

7. Valves for water-column shut-off (2 pages)
   - *a.* Three views of valve (valve open, lock engaged; valve closed, lock disengaged; dimensions)
   - *b.* Valve uses; Code requirements
   - *c.* Tabulation of weights, dimensions, figure number
   - *d.* Two installation views and descriptive text
   - *e.* Related equipment built by firm (2 photos)

8. Back cover (1 page)
   - *a.* Related equipment for high-pressure boilers
   - *b.* Seatless valves (2 views)
   - *c.* Hard-seat valves (2 views)
   - *d.* Unit-tandem valves (2 views)
   - *e.* Descriptive text about each valve; numbers of catalogs covering each valve

f. Listing of other Yarway equipment

g. Company name and address

h. List of cities and countries in which sales representatives are located

When preparing your outline try to visualize the information the typical user will be seeking. Arrange the outline so the needed information is given in the sequence the user will need it. Though there are no fixed rules, many engineers prefer to see the information presented in the following order: (*a*) catalog contents, (*b*) product uses, (*c*) materials of construction, (*d*) product features, (*e*) product ratings, capacities, loads, etc., (*f*) selection procedure, (*g*) product dimensions, weights, color, finish, etc., (*h*) product prices, (*i*) ordering procedure, (*j*) extract of a typical specification for ordering the product, (*k*) typical users, (*l*) sales representatives, (*m*) home office information, (*n*) other related products.

Study your outline and revise it until you're satisfied it's the best you can prepare. Indicate where you'll use illustrations. Specify which illustration will be used where. It's amazing how quickly you can forget which photo you intended to use on page 2, or page 19.

Write a rough draft of your catalog. When you write, keep these rules in mind. Be specific. Be concise. Be concrete. Leave the adjectives at home the day you write your catalog. Give enough information to the catalog user to invite further action on his part. Relate the illustrations to the text. Refer to each illustration if possible. Use short, specific captions for the illustrations.

Don't discourage your reader with pages of formidable text. Break up your text with illustrations, tabulations, and lists of applications of the product.

Be sure your reader knows exactly what the catalog covers. Keep the text short enough to encourage reading. But give the needed facts. Remember—catalog users are looking for a quick, exact answer. Forget the history of your company, how long the firm spent testing the product, and how many generations have used the product. The salesman can supply this information if the customer wants it.

Make all detail drawings large. Be sure the user can read the dimensions. And give those important limiting dimensions—like how much clearance is needed for installation, how close two units can be placed, etc. Don't overlook weights, colors, finishes, materials, and special considerations. They're extremely important to the user of your catalog.

Never overlook product sizes, capacities, figure numbers, models and other variations. Chances are that your product will exactly fill the special needs of certain customers. If it does, you've got a sale.

And show illustrations of related products. But use judgment in this. Don't show auto tires in a catalog on radiator valves. There is hardly ever a customer who needs both at the same time. Instead, include items like radiators, radiator traps, piping, etc., in a catalog on radiator valves. These are items the user might logically need, besides the valves which he was originally looking for in your catalog.

If at all possible, include examples of product selection. When it's necessary for your reader to compute capacity, size, rating, or some other factor, give him several worked-out examples showing him how to make the computation. The catalogs that get the most use in engineering offices are those that save the user time.

Use tabulations, charts, and formulas, in that order, to present selection and product physical data. Arrange the data so that they can be read easily, without a need of squinting.

If your product has limitations—and almost all do—state exactly what these limitations are. Then your users will make fewer mistakes, and there will be less dissatisfaction with your product. Though catalog writing is less restrained than the style used in articles, papers, and books, watch the superlatives. They can get you into trouble.

Check your facts. Once your rough draft is finished, type it neatly and collect all your illustrations. Send the copy and art to the engineering and sales departments for checking. Never begin final production of a catalog until you've done this.

Engineering and sales will probably have comments. Listen to them. Then make the changes they request. But don't let the sales department inject too many adjectives or superlatives into your copy. The back-slapping that gets into many catalogs annoys most engineers. Why? Because they are usually modest people who state the facts and go on from there. So be clear; be brief; give the facts. That's enough for most catalog users.

Polish the rough draft. Use the hints given in Chapters 9, 13, and

17, in this book. Then you'll be certain that your copy is as good as you can make it.

Send to production. Don't skimp on catalog production. Use the best paper, printer, and binding your budget will stand. Remember—your catalog subtly reflects your company. So settle for only the best. You'll never regret it. In general, you'll get better results if you deal with an experienced advertising or publicity agency when producing catalogs. Good industrial agencies have long experience and can advise you what to do.

CATALOGS ARE IMPORTANT

Don't ever ignore catalogs. They're one of the strongest links between your firm and the purchasing public. And since most purchasers today are well-trained technical personnel, the importance of good catalogs will continue to grow.

In a survey of a committee of 100 prominent engineers, *Consulting Engineer* magazine made these findings:

Somewhere between a half and two-thirds of the catalogs received in the mail or directly from salesmen are filed in the wastebasket. This is because too many catalogs contain more sales story than pertinent technical data. The consulting engineer does not want the two combined.

Some manufacturers seem to have a tendency to include not only promotional material but also maintenance and operation manuals and perhaps histories of their companies or detailed reports of the preliminary research required for development of their product. Most of this is superfluous from the consulting engineer's point of view. His primary concern is preparing good specifications for his client.

Contents of a Good Catalog

A good catalog should contain, as a minimum: A brief description of the product, pointing out its special features or characteristics. Complete technical data including ratings and detailed dimensions. Clear statements as to the product's limitations as well as its proper applications. Prices wherever possible.

Generally speaking, consulting engineers prefer tabular data to charts, and prefer charts to formulas. Some charts are quite useful, but they are seldom as easy to read or as accurate as tabular data. Formulas should be avoided except when absolutely essential.

The Committee emphasized most strongly the need for adequate dimensional drawings. It seems that the majority of manufacturers fail to put all of the dimensions required on their product drawings, and they frequently forget to show required clearances. Nothing is more frustrating to the engineer than to find missing from the catalog drawing one of the dimensions he needs.

The engineer also likes to have complete information on the physical and chemical properties of all materials and complete ratings on all equipment. This is particularly important in connection with new products.

One other interesting point from this important survey will be of use to you when you prepare catalogs:

Engineers, as might be expected, prefer catalogs in which specification data is referred to as "engineering data." They strongly object to bulletins in which all technical material is labeled "architects' data." The consulting engineer is particularly offended when the manufacturer addresses himself to architects in connection with products that are obviously within the specification area of engineers. However, the engineer will forgive this if the manufacturers will make a real effort to provide better technical information.

INDUSTRIAL ADVERTISING—A QUICK LOOK

As a technical writer you'll seldom have to write an ad from scratch. Instead, your job will be *rewriting* ads. Sometimes this may mean changing only one word, comma, or colon. At other times you may have to recast whole sentences or paragraphs. But with the high proficiency of industrial ad agencies today you'll seldom have to rewrite an entire ad. Hence our coverage of industrial advertising here will be extremely brief.

Purpose of industrial advertising. Study a few good industrial ads and you'll find that most aim at one or more of the following: (1) finding new markets for established products, or markets for new products, (2) helping spread news of product uses, (3) helping customers get better use from products already purchased, (4) inviting inquiries about new or established products, (5) helping keep the firm ahead of its competitors, and (6) reducing the number of complaints to the service department.

It's almost impossible for a single ad to serve all these purposes.

So you'll find the range and scope of industrial advertising a constant challenge.

Almost every industrial ad is composed of three elements—copy, illustrations, and layout. By *copy* we mean the words—headline and text—in the ad. (At times *copy* is used to mean the entire ad—text, illustrations, and layout.) And since this is a book on writing, we'll neglect the mechanics of preparing an advertising layout. For the art director has more responsibility for the layout than the copywriter.

SIX RULES FOR WRITING GOOD COPY

Industrial advertising is big business. *Business Week* says, "There are about 7,000 periodicals published in the United States. Of these, more than 2,000 are business papers, a group that is thriving as American industry expands." So don't ever slight an industrial ad. It deserves every bit of your skill, ingenuity, and effort. Good advertising has been one of the main forces behind the rise of many outstanding industrial firms in the United States today.

There is no magic formula for writing good copy. But the following rules, if followed sensibly, should help you turn out good copy.

1. Know your readers. You can't write convincing ad copy unless you know who will be reading it. So before you start to write find out where the ad will run. Then write your copy to fit the readers.

The copy you write for *Business Week* certainly would not be suitable for a technical ad in *Water & Sewage Works*. These two magazines have two different kinds of readers, with different interests. If you want readership and action from your ad you must pitch it to the reader's job interests.

Where can you learn who reads a given publication? There are a number of sources of such information. The publication itself will supply a comprehensive analysis. Standard Rate and Data Service is another excellent source of readership data. And your ad agency (if you're employed by an industrial firm) is a reliable source of information about typical readers, their interests, needs, and preferences.

Study the readership data you obtain. Try to form an accurate mental picture of the man or woman you'll aim your ad at. If you can't seem to visualize your typical reader, get out and meet as many actual readers as you can. Visit them on the job. Make notes on how they talk, what their problems are, the atmosphere in which they work. Go

back to your office and study your notes. Your typical reader will come
to life. Then write your copy for him.

2. *Make your ad say something.* Readers of business magazines are
busy people. But at the same time they're anxious to learn. If your ad
speaks the reader's language and tells him something that will help him
on the job, he'll read your copy. But if your ad lacks facts, it won't be
read. It isn't worth the reader's time.

So before you start to write, have something to say. If you don't
know what to say, stop and find out. Empty ads waste money, magazine space, and valuable time.

What will your ad say? Any of a thousand things. But if you've
read many industrial ads you'll find most stress an advantage of some
kind. Typical advantages popular today are (*a*) saving of time, money,
effort, space, weight, labor, etc., and (*b*) better product quality, service, life, reliability, and performance. Here are typical ad headlines
which say different but specific things:

Reduced voltage starters . . . easy on the motor . . . easy on the line

Solve difficult liquid processing problems

Silicone insulated motors help keep production moving

700% longer service with these Crane valves

Maintaining *maximum* flow in serum lines with *minimum* pressure drop

Versatile starch system steps up capacity

Again: Make your ad say something. You'll get better readership,
action. If you don't know what to say, find out. Keep in mind that the
usual reader reads his magazine *at* work. Say something he wants to
hear. This will ensure the readership you deserve.

3. *Keep your message simple.* Few of your readers are Ph.D.'s. Most
are working men, struggling to do the best job possible. Speak in terms
they can understand at a glance, like these:

Pellets cut costs

These Reliance meters will not corrode

Underwater, underground—this hose loves its salt diet

Emphasize the product. There's no doubt what the three ads above
cover—pellets, motors, hose. If the reader is interested in any of these
you can be sure he'll read the ad.

Don't deal in complicated symbols. If you're writing an ad about industrial hoses, talk about hoses—not symbols like fluid highways, liquid conduits, etc. These are one step removed from hoses. And your reader wants information on hoses—regardless of how prosaic this word may seem.

So decide what you want to say—then say it in as simple and as direct a manner as possible. And be sure your message relates to the reader's job. If he wants to read about golf clubs or skin-diving equipment he'll buy a magazine covering these. In his business magazine he wants, and expects to get, business information.

Make your headline forceful, interesting, attention-getting. Don't go highbrow—stick to the simple message, like:

Now, a giant in capacity . . . yet moderate in size

Pumping molten chemicals? Write Taber

A package for pollution control

4. Tell your story with pictures. Show your reader what you mean. Give him a photo of the unit, a chart to compute capacity, a cutaway drawing showing how the device works. Pictures get your story across to the reader faster, save words, attract more attention. And if you're using photos, try to include installation views of the product. Engineers and scientists prefer installation shots. There's much to be learned from how the other guy piped up his unit or braced a foundation. Avoid the symbol type of photo—dogs, cats, lions, seals, etc. They mean little. Instead, show your product. That's what your reader is interested in seeing.

Next to photos, charts and graphs are most popular. Try to use a chart or graph that gives information of value to the reader. A pretty but unusable chart means little. Present a chart or graph and show the reader how it will solve a problem for *him*.

Cutaway views have many applications—machines, buildings, ships, planes, and various equipment. But don't clutter the cutaway with type that obstructs the construction details. Never forget that your readers are scientifically trained. They want to learn how the other designer, engineer, chemist, or geologist solved a problem. Show them—use cutaways.

Steer clear of frills, scrolls, and all other fancy designs around the illustrations in your ad. Use a simple rectangular or square photo, drawing, or chart. The scientific mind is geometric-conscious. So leave the frills for consumer ads and concentrate on the simple illustration that shows your product clearly.

5. Be helpful—it never hurts. Your reader wants help with the problems he meets on his job. If you help him—he'll buy your product. Take a look at a few ads stressing help (only the headline and first paragraphs are given):

Why Celanese chose these mixers for *low-pressure polyethylene*
    How can mechanical mixers help you give the touch of success to an important new process?
        Celanese Corporation of America faced this question when its Plastics Division designed a plant to produce 100,000 lbs/day of. . . .

Here is another ad designed to help the reader solve his problems:

B. F. Goodrich report:
    No holes, no leaks, no repairs—liquid alum stored safely in rubber
    Problem: This paper manufacturer wanted to cut costs by switching from powdered to liquid alum in their pulp mixture. But getting a tank to hold this corrosive solution was a problem. Wood tanks shrink, often leak. Lead-lined tanks require frequent repairs.
    What was done: B. F. Goodrich engineers recommended Triflex rubber-lining for the two 5,000-gallon steel storage tanks. . . .

Aiming at the major problems of many engineers helps get your message across:

Get product uniformity faster and at less cost . . . with NETTCO Engineered Agitation

Increase productivity, lower power costs, and minimize maintenance requirements . . . with "process-rated" Model WT agitators . . .

When you offer help, be sure your claims for the product are fair. Don't exaggerate! You'll only cause more grief and trouble. State what your product will do. Then stop.

6. Keep your ad professional. Speak the language of your readers. Don't introduce unnecessary chatter or unrelated information. State your claims, and document each claim with simple, unassailable facts. Then your readers will be more likely to ask for more information.

This can eventually lead to the sale of the product or service you're aiming at.

INDUSTRIAL AD HEADLINES

If you're going to catch a reader, you'll probably do it with an interesting headline. For almost everything in an ad depends on an effective headline.

Two rules will help you write better headlines: (1) Strive for complete clarity in the headline. (2) Tie the headline in with the illustrations in the ad.

Clarity is of utmost importance because business-paper readers are busy people. They haven't time to spend trying to decipher a trick headline. So state your facts clearly and interestingly, the way these examples do:

Modern, efficient NINEMILE POINT plant uses modern, efficient turbine oil: GULFCREST

"Big Station" combustion controls pay off for packaged boiler plant

The blow-off valve trend on "package" boilers is YARWAY SEATLESS

Tying your headline in with the illustrations adds to the effectiveness of both. In the first of the three ads above, two views of the plant named are shown. In the second ad three views of boilers and their control are shown. The third ad features seven illustrations of the product mentioned in the headline. Make your headline and illustrations work together. Your ad will have greater unity, more punch, and fuller meaning.

SUMMARY

Industrial catalogs are important to all technical personnel today. Good catalogs are effective tools in the office and plant. Catalogs have two main jobs—to inform equipment users and motivate sales. Users refer to a catalog *before* calling a salesman. To write effective catalogs you must know the purpose of the catalog, determine its users, decide what to include, and present the information in the best way possible. In actually writing a catalog you must collect data, make an outline, write a rough draft, check your facts, polish the rough draft, and then submit the material to the production department.

Industrial advertising is generally written by ad agencies. But at times you may have to assist in writing or checking ads. Before writing any industrial advertising copy, know whom you're writing for, make your ad say something, keep your message simple, tell your story with pictures, be helpful, and keep your material professional in character. Be sure the headline for your ad is clear, interesting, and ties in with the illustrations in the ad.

CHAPTER CHECK-UP

1. Is writing catalogs and bulletins worthwhile? Why?
2. What two aims should every catalog have? Explain.
3. What do users want from a catalog?
4. What is a catalog? Select two examples of catalogs meeting your definition.
5. List four steps you should take before writing a catalog. Explain each.
6. Name five types of industrial catalogs used today.
7. What kind of catalogs do technical writers usually write?
8. How can you determine who will use your catalog? What must you know about the users?
9. How would you determine what to include in a catalog?
10. Give six steps to follow in writing a catalog. Explain each step.
11. Where can you obtain data and illustrations for catalogs?
12. What kinds of standards should you set for catalog illustrations?
13. Why is an outline important for your catalog?
14. Choose a catalog dealing with a product that interests you. Prepare an outline of its contents. Is the catalog adequate? If not, show how it could be improved.
15. Give the preferred contents sequence for industrial catalogs.
16. What should you keep in mind while writing a catalog? Explain.
17. How should detail drawings be made?
18. Should you show related products in a catalog? Explain.
19. When should you use tabulations, charts, or formulas? What is the preferred order for these elements?
20. How can you check the facts in your catalog? When should you make changes in the text or illustrations? Why?
21. Give the steps in polishing the catalog text. Explain each step.
22. Why are catalogs important?
23. What do engineers like and dislike in industrial catalogs? Explain.
24. What is the purpose of industrial advertising? Discuss.
25. What is the typical industrial ad composed of? Discuss each element.

26. Give six rules for writing industrial advertising copy. Discuss each rule in detail.
27. Why must you know your reader?
28. Why must your ad say something? How can you be sure it will?
29. Should your message be simple or complex? Why? Give examples of six good ads. Show why they are effective.
30. Why are illustrations important in ads? What kinds of illustrations are preferred? Explain.
31. How can you keep ads professional?
32. Why is the ad headline important? Give six examples of good headlines and tell why you consider them good.

Chapter 15

TECHNICAL BOOKS—
THE ULTIMATE CHALLENGE

In Chapter 1 you learned the many advantages you secure from writing good technical material. Review these advantages now by reading Chapter 1 again. Pay particular attention to the information on books. The technical book, since it is far longer than a technical article, is a much more difficult writing task. But the rewards are in proportion to the extra work required. A good technical book has a long life, contributes much to the knowledge of your field, and can be an important factor in your personal finances. Also, the prestige you acquire from a well-written book can do much to further your career.

KINDS OF TECHNICAL BOOKS

What kind of books do engineers, scientists, and technicians write? There are many types, but they can be roughly classed in seven categories: (1) home-study texts, (2) technical training texts, (3) college texts, (4) industrial reference books, (5) advanced engineering books, (6) engineering monographs, and (7) handbooks. Let's take a look at each type.

1. *Home-study texts.* These are designed for use by men and women who wish to increase their knowledge by spare-time study. Since the student usually has no instructor other than the book, you must be extremely careful in this type of writing. You must put yourself in the reader's place and try to visualize what questions will occur to

him as he uses your text. These questions should be answered in the explanatory portion of your book.

Two prime requirements of the home-study type of book are (*a*) clear writing, and (*b*) enough illustrative and study problems to allow the reader to get a firm grasp of the subject matter. Of course clear, easily understood writing is essential in every technical book, but as an author of the home-study type you must take extra precautions to make yourself understood. If you do not, you may find yourself swamped by letters from users of your book!

Illustrative problems show how to perform the steps described in the text of your book. Study problems give the reader opportunity for practice and self-testing. You should include the answers to the study problems so that the reader can check his work. Avoid trick problems. The reason for this is that your reader has no one to turn to when he meets a problem that is confusing or misleading.

To get a better concept of this type of book, refer to the two following examples: W. S. LaLonde, "Professional Engineers' Examination Questions and Answers," McGraw-Hill Book Company, Inc., New York, 1956; Aaron Axelrod, "Machine Shop Mathematics," McGraw-Hill Book Company, Inc., New York, 1951.

2. Technical-training texts. These may or may not be more advanced in subject matter than books written for home-study use. The usual text of this type is prepared for study by candidates for training for technician-level jobs in industry. These are usually high school graduates having the fundamental training in physics and chemistry given in secondary schools. So you can use a higher-level approach in the technical-training text than you can in the usual home-study text.

Good technical training texts are characterized by clear, simple writing, combined with careful matching of the text and illustrations. These characteristics are desirable in every technical book; however, the extra effort you make to produce an outstanding technical training text is appreciated by all your readers.

Two examples of technical training texts are "Automotive Engines," W. H. Crouse, McGraw-Hill Book Company, Inc., 1955, and "Basic Television," Bernard Grob, McGraw-Hill Book Company, Inc., 1954.

3. College texts. These are most frequently written by teachers in engineering schools and by part-time faculty members. Relatively few engineers and technicians in industry can write a text specifically for use in colleges. But some of the books written by engineers in industry are adopted as college texts. Most books of this type that are adopted are also of interest to engineers in the field, and are usually written for them. College adoption comes later. Keep these facts in mind when you think about writing a text for college use.

Occasionally college texts are coauthored by an engineer on the teaching staff and an engineer in industry. Each contributes his particular talent and knowledge to produce a well-balanced coverage. Collaborating with a teacher is probably the best way for you to author a college text if you are not a faculty member yourself.

Two typical examples of outstanding college texts are "Engineering Drawing," Frank Zozzora, McGraw-Hill Book Company, Inc., 1954, and "Water Supply and Sewerage," E. W. Steel, McGraw-Hill Book Company, Inc., 1953.

4. Industrial reference books. These are written primarily for engineers, scientists, and technicians working in a particular field. They may also be used by students, salesmen, technicians, and others interested in that field. If you study a number of industrial reference books you will see that this type puts somewhat more emphasis on applications than on theory. This is because the man in the field is most interested in solution of problems related to his job. Theoretical discussions are of little use to him unless he can see some relation between them and his daily work.

Two examples of industrial reference books are "Pumps," Frank Kristal and F. A. Annett, McGraw-Hill Book Company, Inc., 1953, and "Water Conditioning for Industry," S. T. Powell, McGraw-Hill Book Company, Inc., 1954.

5. Advanced engineering books. These differ from industrial reference books in a number of ways. In general, the advanced engineering book is more theoretical. It is directed at a higher audience level and is likely to have a mathematical approach. The subject matter generally deals more with design and engineering considerations than with the problems of installation, operation, and maintenance. There are, of course, some variations in these characteristics, but they are typical of many advanced engineering books today. Keep these in mind when you think of writing an advanced engineering book.

Two typical examples of this group are "Electronic Semiconductors," Eberhard Spenke, McGraw-Hill Book Company, Inc., 1958, and "Bearing Design and Application," D. F. Wilcock and E. R. Booser, McGraw-Hill Book Company, Inc., 1957.

6. *Engineering monographs.* These books usually cover a limited area of a particular field. Instead of giving a broad, limited-depth view of a field, as some industrial reference books do, the usual engineering monograph delves deeply, but over a restricted area. A mathematical approach is commonly used. The mathematics may be more rigorous than in an advanced engineering book.

The Engineering Society Monographs, sponsored by AIEE, ASCE, AIME, and ASME, are probably the best examples of books of this type. Two titles available today in this series are "Hydraulic Transients," G. R. Rich, McGraw-Hill Book Company, Inc., 1951, and "Theory of Elasticity," S. P. Timoshenk and J. N. Goodier, McGraw-Hill Book Company, Inc., 1951. The engineering monograph has a long life because its approach is basic.

7. *Handbooks.* These are not "written," in the same sense as most other technical books are. Instead, there are a number of contributors, often more than 50, each of whom writes a portion or section of the book. These sections are submitted to the editor of the handbook, who works the material into a unified coverage of the subject matter. To achieve this, the editor may restyle some of the material submitted but he never alters its factual content. When the handbook editor is a specialist in some phase of a field, as is often the case, he may write one or more sections of the handbook himself.

In many ways, editing a handbook is the ultimate in technical authorship. You must have long experience in your profession and a high degree of writing skill before you can qualify for handbook editorship. A wide acquaintance with the outstanding members of the profession covered by the handbook is another necessity if a large number of contributors is contemplated.

Two examples of modern engineering handbooks are "Radio Engineering Handbook," Keith Henney, McGraw-Hill Book Company, Inc., 1959, and "Chemical Engineers' Handbook," John Perry, McGraw-Hill Book Company, Inc., 1950. Most engineering handbooks have a long life because their approach is fundamental.

WHO USES BOOKS

Though a rough classification of typical books written by engineers, scientists, and technicians is easily set up, as we have done here, it is extremely difficult to predict the final users of a given book. For example a home-study text might find use in technical-training and college courses. Many handbooks are used in college courses. Industrial reference books, advanced engineering books, and monographs are used up and down the scale of readership. Book use depends on the needs of the user.

So you should regard the classification given above merely as a device to aid you in understanding the range and scope of technical books written today. You can control what goes into your book but that's where your jurisdiction ends. Users are free to choose books that appeal to them, and the variety of their choice is often surprising.

WHAT MAKES A GOOD BOOK

Deciding to write a technical book can be one of the most important decisions in your career, for a well-written book can, to repeat, bring you prestige, recognition, a feeling of accomplishment, and financial returns of generous proportions. Not only that, a good technical book is a permanent contribution to the literature of your profession. As such it stands for all to see—the bench mark of one engineer or scientist who had the energy and ability to do something to help his fellows in the daily problems of engineering or science.

But such returns are not easily won. Writing a good technical book is a challenging and arduous task. It takes enthusiasm, skill, energy, and a sincere desire to help others. That it can be done is proved every time a good book is published. Now let's take a look at the factors that go into the writing of an outstanding technical book.

An outstanding technical book usually meets all of the following five requirements: (1) It answers the specific questions of its intended readers. (2) It takes a comprehensive view of the subject covered. (3) It is scrupulously accurate in text and illustration. (4) It takes progressive steps from the known to the unknown—from the reader's viewpoint. (5) It is written in a clear, simple, grammatical manner, organized to present the subject matter logically and effectively. An outstanding technical book is not only a work of science; it also approaches a work of art. The following chapters cover many of the important problems you meet in writing a technical book of any kind.

WORDS OF CAUTION

Before you decide to write any technical book consider the implications of your decision. Experience indicates that the average author of a technical book spends at least one year writing it. Why? Consider this. Most technical books have between 10 and 20 chapters. You will find that if you write your book in your spare time that the average chapter requires about one month. So you can see that with 10 or 15 chapters you will spend approximately one year actually writing your book.

In terms of words and illustrations, the average technical book presents a major challenge to any writer. For example, a book containing 300 published pages will have 50,000 to 100,000 words, depending upon the number of illustrations. The usual technical book published today contains about one illustration per page. In a 300-page book you are likely to find between 200 and 300 illustrations.

Since you must either draw or obtain each illustration from an outside source, it is easy to see that you can spend much time just securing illustrations. If you type your manuscript so that it has an average of 12 words per line, which is usually the case, you will find that you must have between 4,000 and 8,000 lines of typewritten material for the text of your book. And since the usual double-spaced typewritten page contains 25 lines, your manuscript will consist of somewhere between 160 and 400 typewritten pages. Many authors find that just the physical preparation of their manuscript is a major undertaking.

Besides the physical preparation of the text and illustrations, the writer of a technical book must have the necessary know-how. Since it is impossible for you to know everything about the subject matter of your book you will probably have to do some research. This, of course, takes time. And you will have to secure permission from publishers to use copyrighted material assembled in the course of your research. To secure such permission you must write the copyright owner. This, too, takes time.

Besides all the work that you put into the book you must be ready to accept and use the criticisms of the reviewers of your manuscript. Some reviewers are extremely critical of the material they read. While such criticisms may upset the new author, experienced authors learn to disregard the bite in the critic's remarks. The experienced writer takes all the critic's worthwhile points and tries to include them in his manuscript. Some authors find it difficult to learn to do this without becoming upset.

HOW YOU CAN WRITE YOUR BOOK

There are four ways of writing your book. These are: (1) as the sole author, (2) with one coauthor, (3) with more than one co-author, and (4) with contributors. Let's take a quick look at each of these schemes.

One author. Here you write the entire book yourself. You may secure help from others but the major writing task is yours. You must also secure the illustrations yourself, although your associates may be kind enough to supply some for your book.

When writing a book by yourself you must meet and solve a large number of minor problems. The first problem you run into when thinking of a book is: What type shall it be? Shall it be a home-study text, shall it be an industrial reference book, or shall it be a textbook? Although a publisher can give you a little help with this decision, you will find that you must take most of the responsibility yourself. Additional decisions that you will have to make during the writing of your book include such things as chapter length, the number and types of illustrations to use, and the style of writing. As you can see, all of these decisions require time and energy.

Although the effort required in writing a book by yourself is a major task, there is the consoling thought that the returns come to you alone. You acquire any prestige that the book commands; you receive the royalties from the sale of the book. With any other arrangement you must share both the prestige and (usually) the royalties.

Before deciding to author a book by yourself think carefully. You should have had some previous writing experience—the more the better. You should be able to construct a good outline and you should be willing to follow the advice of books like the one you are reading, as well as the advice that your publisher may offer you.

While the strong individualist may appear to be a romantic character, the successful technical author today is the man or woman who is willing to listen to and take advice from others in the publishing business.

Two coauthors. In this arrangement you work with some man or woman in producing your book. The exact scheme used depends upon the individual situation. In many cases the work will be split equally between the two authors. For example, one will write the first half of the book while the second writes the other half. Each secures his own illustrations. Another scheme teams an author having a great amount of practical know-how but relatively little writing talent with an experienced writer with less technical knowledge. Here the experienced man gains the advantage of having a well-qualified writer prepare his material.

For two authors coauthorship can be an extremely successful undertaking. But the temperament of one author must mesh with that of the other. Otherwise you may find that one of the coauthors is doing much more than his share of the work. This can lead to misunderstanding and difficulty.

Often two authors share the royalties from the book equally. Other arrangements, of course, are possible. For example one author may receive 20 per cent and the other 80 per cent of the royalties. The exact split does not concern the publisher. But every publisher is interested in seeing that both coauthors are satisfied with any arrangement that is decided upon.

If you are considering authoring a book with someone else, the best advice that you can be given is to select your coauthor with as much care as you would a wife or a husband. Some engineers and scientists overlook the important personal aspects of coauthorship. In forgetting that their coauthor is a human being they fail to anticipate the problems that may arise. So before becoming a coauthor or asking someone else to become a coauthor, think carefully. Once you decide to coauthor a book with someone, make it perfectly clear exactly what you expect of him and what you will contribute.

To obtain the maximum benefit from a dual-authorship arrangement you should set up a schedule of deadlines for each coauthor. Arrange and understand how your correspondence or other communications will be carried out. Keep informed at all times of the progress of your coauthor and be careful to inform him of exactly what you have accomplished. If two people are completely honest with each other, joint authorship can be an extremely pleasant and rewarding experience.

More than two authors. Much the same arrangement is used with three or more authors as with two. But instead of the work's being divided between two people, three or more do the work. Once again each of the authors must be carefully chosen and definite arrangements must be made for the amount of work to be done and the manner of communication between the authors. If you carefully plan how the work will be divided and how the communication will be carried on, a major task in the writing of your book will be solved.

Here again the personalities of the authors involved are crucial. They must all have a common aim. If they do not the book may turn out to be a failure. If possible, one of the authors should assume the responsibility of seeing that the other authors deliver their material on time and that it is of satisfactory quality. Often the man who originates the idea for the book fulfills this function.

Contributors. The contributed book is usually a handbook. As we said above, each contributor writes a section or chapter. The section assigned any contributor is one with which he is completely familiar. A chief editor correlates the work of all the contributors. Instead of sharing in the royalties, as do the coauthors under the two previous arrangements, a contributor is usually paid a flat fee for his work by the editor. This is based on the number of published pages in the contributor's section.

Reference books and text books are also sometimes written by a number of contributors. The plan is the same as for a handbook, but on a smaller scale. All the recommendations made above in connection with coauthorship apply to the contributed book, whether handbook, textbook, or reference book.

QUALIFICATIONS FOR TECHNICAL BOOK AUTHORSHIP

No two authors of technical books are exactly the same, of course. However they all have some characteristics in common. These are: (1) thorough knowledge of a specific subject, (2) a strong desire to help or inform others about their subject, (3) ability to write clearly, and (4) a sense of organization—that is the ability to see and plan a major project in an effective and logical way.

No doubt many books have been written by authors who lack one or more of these characteristics. But the outstanding technical author usually has at least three of them. So before you decide to write a technical book give some thought to your own characteristics. If you find that you more or less fill the bill, you can be reasonably sure of being successful.

It may seem strange that in this chapter concerning technical authorship there are many remarks of a personal nature. But, after all, the writing of a book is much more than just putting facts on paper. Though the task requires primarily the use of your talents and abilities, your entire personality becomes involved. Unless you have the needed temperament as well as the needed skills, you may find it is impossible to complete your book. And since failure to complete a book is always a major disappointment, it is best that you have the complete situation in your mind before deciding to go ahead with a technical book.

SUMMARY

There are about seven kinds of technical books being written today. Each fills a definite need in its primary field. But many technical books are used up and down the scale of reader educational level. To be outstanding, a technical book must meet a number of requirements, from the standpoint of both subject matter and writing skill. You can write a book by yourself, or with the aid of one or more coauthors. The method you choose depends on your own technical knowledge, writing skill, and professional experience.

CHAPTER CHECK-UP

1. Name seven kinds of technical books popular today.
2. What are the main characteristics of home-study texts?
3. How should home-study texts be written to be of most use?
4. What is a technical-training text? Where is this kind of book used?
5. List the characteristics of well-prepared technical-training texts.
6. What is a college text? Who usually authors a college text? Why?

7. How do industrial reference books differ from college texts? For whom are reference books usually written?
8. What is an advanced engineering book? What are its usual characteristics?
9. Describe an engineering monograph. How does a monograph differ from other technical books?
10. What is an engineering handbook? How is the usual handbook compiled and edited?
11. State five requirements for an outstanding technical book.
12. Discuss the typical physical elements (number of words, lines, illustrations, etc.) of a 400-page technical book. Estimate the amount of time involved in preparing such a work.
13. Name four ways of authoring a book. Give details of each.
14. What personal characteristics are helpful to an author? Discuss each.

Chapter 16

FINDING AND DEVELOPING
BOOK IDEAS

Finding an idea that can be developed into an outstanding technical book is difficult. An idea for a book usually develops slowly. Article ideas and technical-paper ideas often come quickly. With a little experience you should be able to develop an article idea within a matter of hours after you first think of it. But it may take you many months or even years to develop the ideas for an outstanding technical book. Let's see how some book ideas are found and developed.

FINDING IDEAS FOR TECHNICAL BOOKS

Probably the most common incentives for the writing of engineering and scientific books are (1) the discovery that there are no books covering a particular subject and (2) the realization that the existing books in a field are outdated.

Either of these is sufficient to start you thinking about writing a book on a given subject. But before starting to write a book for either of these reasons give the project careful thought. Also, read the remainder of this chapter.

Book ideas sometimes develop from other types of writing you may do. For example, if you write a series of articles on a given subject you may suddenly discover that you have the nucleus of a book. Or if you prepare several technical papers on your specialty you may find that they are suitable for use as the basis of a technical book. Or you may write lectures, class notes, catalogs, bulletins, or reports that can be worked into a book.

When considering any of these sources of book ideas you must remember that a good technical book is far more comprehensive than an article, technical paper, lecture, catalog, report, or bulletin. A technical book has far greater depth of coverage and scope of subject matter than the usual short technical piece.

A technical book, to be of real value to its readers, must cover a fairly wide portion of its subject. This is important. While the subject itself may be a narrow one—for example, the subject of pumps—you must cover a sufficient number of types of pumps to make the book of use to a wide range of readers. Some beginning writers make the mistake of limiting the scope of coverage of a book. This reduces the potential audience for the book and may make the cost of publication almost prohibitive.

Let's assume you have an idea for a book—the first book you've attempted. What do you do next? Here is one procedure that has worked successfully for a large number of technical authors throughout the world. Study this procedure carefully and see if you can apply it to your idea. With only slight alterations it should be usable for any of the seven types of books we discussed in the previous chapter.

DEVELOPING BOOK IDEAS

The first step to take after you get an idea for a book is to classify the book under one of the headings in the previous chapter. Unless you know what type of book you are trying to write it will be extremely difficult to do a good job.

So consider your idea carefully. Shall your book be a home-study text? Shall it be an industrial reference book? Shall it be a college text? Or shall it be an advanced engineering text? Decide which category your book will fill.

Once you have decided the type of book you plan to write, your next step is to secure from four to six representative examples of this type. You can secure these from a good library or you can purchase them. Read each of them carefully. Note the style that each author uses in his writing. Observe how many chapters the author uses. Study the subheads, paragraphing, tabulations, illustrative examples, and student exercise material in each of the books.

The idea in studying examples in this way is not to imitate the works of others. Rather, it is to stimulate your own ideas. Once you have written a technical book it will not be necessary for you to study the work of others. But for your first book it is wise for you to learn as much as possible about how other people work. Never over-look this step in developing a book idea. You can learn a great deal from the work of other authors.

Note that the books you study need not have the same subject matter as you plan to cover in your book. But if there is a book on the same or a similar subject as yours there is no harm in seeing how the author arranged his subject matter. While studying these books you should also observe the number and type of illustrations the author used, and their sources.

In your examination of books you will find some authors whose work you admire. Other books may not appeal to you. Discard the books that you feel are not up to the level that you would like to attain. Note that you are not examining the books for subject matter; you are attempting to learn the way a book is put together from the standpoint of chapters, paragraphs, illustrations, etc.

You will find that most well-written technical books follow a logical line of thought from the known to the unknown. You will also observe that the writer is extremely careful to consider his readers with every word he chooses, every sentence he writes, and every chapter he develops. So do not skip this extremely important phase of developing your idea into an outstanding book.

YOU MUST OUTLINE

Never attempt to write a technical book without a comprehensive outline. While some books have been written without an outline, the resulting product is seldom outstanding. The shortest road to misery and pain in writing a technical book is to attempt the task without an outline.

Even experienced writers sometimes have difficulty writing an article without an outline; writing a first book without one will almost surely prove an unmanageable task.

You must remember that just the physical size of a book in terms of manuscript pages and illustrations is enormous compared with any other writing you may have done. This massive bulk can quickly go astray unless you have it under adequate control. And your best control is a good outline.

There are two steps in outlining a book. These are: (1) Prepare a chapter outline. (2) Prepare an outline of each chapter in the book.

Think of the first step as giving you an over-all view of your entire book. Once you have prepared this outline you will be able to judge if the balance of the various phases of the subject matter is suitable for your readers. If your plan devotes too much space to one phase of your subject, this will probably be apparent in the over-all chapter outline.

While preparing the over-all chapter outline, note alongside the name of each chapter how many printed pages you would like to devote to that chapter. "But," you say, "I do not know how many pages that chapter should have." If you don't know, guess. Ask yourself how important this chapter is to the reader and to the subject matter you cover. If the chapter is extremely important it deserves more space than a less important chapter. If you are introducing difficult concepts you are likely to need more space than if you are reviewing some material that the reader is probably familiar with.

As you recall, in the last chapter we noted that writing a book requires that you make a series of small decisions. This over-all chapter outline and the selection of the number of pages for each chapter is an excellent example of the decisions that will constantly face you while you are writing your book. If you do not start to make the decisions early in your book you will have an extremely difficult time with the text.

Once you have finished your over-all chapter outline, you should begin your individual chapter outline. As you proceed with this outline you will probably find it necessary to change the number of published pages you tentatively assigned to certain chapters in the over-all chapter outline. Do not be afraid to change the numbers. For when you are finished with your individual chapter outline you will go back and add up the various page numbers. For the usual technical book published by a commercial publisher today the total number of printed pages should run somewhere between 100 and 400.

While shorter technical books are occasionally published today, and also longer ones, your first effort should be within the range that publishers prefer. Today this is 100 to 400 printed pages.

When preparing your individual chapter outline it is wise to make it as specific as possible. If you skip work now you will have more to do later. But if you make a complete outline now you will be free later to concentrate on writing. You will be free of the burden of worry lest you have left out something important. And consequently you will write a better book.

In a word, the outline is designed to save you work. So do not regard it as a nuisance. Actually, a good outline allows you to write a better book in shorter time with less effort. Of course you will probably make some minor changes in your outline as you write your book. This should cause you no concern. But if you feel you must make major changes in your outline, you should stop writing and review the entire project, because this usually indicates that there is an unbalance in the division of your subject matter. Do not hesitate to revamp your outline if necessary. The effort required is usually slight compared to rewriting a major portion of your book.

TYPICAL OUTLINES

Two typical outlines of published books are given below. The first is for an industrial reference book and the second is for an engineering handbook. While neither of these outlines could be adapted to a book you might write they are both extremely useful for study. They illustrate many points we have discussed in the text of this chapter.

The subject matter of the industrial reference book was such that it could be divided into three major sections. Thus when studying the over-all chapter outline you will note that the book is divided into three parts. This was done because dividing the book into parts made it easier to achieve a unity within each part. This is extremely important, and you should consider the possibility of dividing your book into parts. Not only does the division into parts contribute to unity; you will find that the divisions aid your thinking and act as inventory-taking points during your writing.

Since writing a technical book is a task involving a large number of words and illustrations, you can often help yourself by setting up a series of small deadlines to act as mileposts. Both part and chapter divisions provide such mileposts for you. Reaching any milepost gives you a sense of accomplishment. It also means that you are nearer the end of your task. And don't think you won't be glad when you come to the end of the book, no matter how much of a pleasure it has been to write it.

Reference book outline. The following outline was prepared before any writing was done on the book. Note that the estimated number of printed pages in the over-all chapter outline was 400. The actual number of published pages was 432. This illustrates how closely you can control the published length of a book if you prepare an accurate and well-organized outline.

Over-all Chapter Outline
"Pump Selection and Application"

Part 1 *Pump Classes and Types*
    Chapter 1. Centrifugal Pumps   24 pages
    Chapter 2. Rotary Pumps   7 pages
    Chapter 3. Reciprocating Pumps   28 pages
Part 2 *Factors in Pump Selection*
    Chapter 4. Head on a Pump   25 pages
    Chapter 5. Pump Capacity   29 pages
    Chapter 6. Liquid Handled   31 pages
    Chapter 7. Piping Systems   48 pages
    Chapter 8. Drives for Pumps   20 pages
    Chapter 9. Pump Selection   14 pages
    Chapter 10. System Economics   25 pages
Part 3 *Pump Application*
    Chapter 11. Power Services   15 pages
    Chapter 12. Nuclear Energy   10 pages
    Chapter 13. Petroleum Industry   12 pages
    Chapter 14. Chemical Industries   15 pages
    Chapter 15. Paper, Textiles   11 pages
    Chapter 16. Food Processing   9 pages
    Chapter 17. Water Supply   14 pages
    Chapter 18. Sewage and Sump   10 pages
    Chapter 19. Air Conditioning   10 pages
    Chapter 20. Irrigation   9 pages
    Chapter 21. Mining, Construction   8 pages
    Chapter 22. Marine Services   11 pages
    Chapter 23. Hydraulic Services   10 pages
    Chapter 24. Iron, Steel   5 pages

Total page count   400 pages

Individual Chapter Outline
"Pump Selection and Application"

Part I   *Pump Classes and Types*

Chapter 1.   Centrifugal Pumps
  A. Pump classes
     Centrifugal
     Rotary
     Reciprocating
  B. Types of centrifugal pumps
     Volute
     Diffuser
     Turbine
     Mixed-flow
     Propeller
     Jet
  C. Broad head-capacity characteristics of each type
  D. Centrifugal pumps classified according to specific applications

Chapter 2.   Rotary Pumps
  A. Types of rotary pumps
     Cam-and-piston
     External-gear
     Internal-gear
     Two-, three-, and four-lobe
     Single-, two-, and three-screw
     Swinging-vane
     Sliding-vane
     Shuttle-block
     Universal-joint
     Eccentric
     Flexible-tube

Chapter 3.   Reciprocating Pumps
  A. Types of reciprocating pumps
     Direct-acting
     Power
     Controlled-volume
     Other types—rotary plunger, hydraulic, diaphragm
  B. Head-capacity characteristics of typical reciprocating pumps
  C. Reciprocating-pump application

C. Internal-combustion engines
D. Factors in drive selection: first and operating costs, availability of electric power, pump speed, etc.
E. Gears, belts, chains

Chapter 9. Pump Selection
A. Pump specifications
B. Inquiry forms
C. Securing the bid
D. Liquid requirements for various services
E. Evaluating bids
F. Ordering the unit

Chapter 10. System Economics
A. The economic analysis; its purpose, scope, use
B. Steps in making an analysis
C. Factors to be considered in the analysis
D. Typical economic analysis for industrial pumping condtions
E. Using an existing pump

Part III *Pump Application*

Chapter 11. Power Services
A. Boiler feed: high-pressure, medium-pressure, low-pressure
B. Condensate, hot-well, heater-drain and return pumps
C. Circulating and cooling-water pumps
D. Ash and abrasive-solids pumps
E. Fuel-oil pumps
F. Chemical-feed and proportioning pumps
G. Internal-combustion engine plants
H. Factors in selecting and applying pumps for the power services

Chapter 12. Nuclear Energy
A. AEC program
B. Service conditions
C. Canned-motor pumps
D. Special designs
E. Pump choice

Chapter 13. Petroleum Industry
A. Pumps for petroleum production: reciprocating, sucker rods, surface equipment; operating characteristics
B. Refinery pumps: general purpose, general process, chemical process; operating requirements for refinery pumps
C. Pipeline pumps: centrifugal—horizontal and vertical units; reciprocating; bulk stations

    B. Descaling
    C. Natural-gas processing
    D. Plastics
    E. Newspapers
    F. Paint manufacture
    G. Cosmetics
    H. Automotive
    I. Electronics
    J. Metalworking

This outline does not contain any information about the number of illustrations to be used in the book. As you recall, however, in the last chapter we noted that many modern technical books have about one illustration per page. This 432-page book has 412 illustrations. The author of this book planned to use about an illustration per page and the results were reasonably accurate.

To learn what the usual preface of a book contains, read several technical books. You will find that the good preface tells *who* you've written the book for, *why* you've written it, and *what* the reader will get from your book. And the preface is the place where you thank anyone who has helped you with your book.

Handbook Outline. The following outline is for a major engineering handbook. As you can see, the over-all section outline of this handbook is relatively short. The individual chapter outlines are quite comprehensive. Study this outline and note how good a concept of the finished book you can acquire from it. This outline proved itself to be an excellent device to control the writing of the book.

Over-all Section Outline
"The Standard Handbook of Lubrication Engineering"

PREFACE: The preface theme will serve as an introduction to the lubrication-engineering profession. There will be a preview of the Handbook's scope, plus a general discussion of the 4-part structural outline:

    Part   I.   Lubrication Principles
    Part II.   General Lubrication Engineering Practice
    Part III.   Lubrication of Specific Equipment
    Part IV.   Lubrication in Specific Industries

Individual Chapter Outline
"The Standard Handbook of Lubrication Engineering"
Part I. Lubrication Principles

Section 1. Concepts

Chapter 1. Dry friction
  1. Sliding
  2. Rolling
  3. Metallic
  4. Nonmetallic
  5. Contact area
  6. Surface roughness
  7. Laws of friction
  8. Energy analysis; surface temperature
  9. Ambient conditions; temperature, pressure, contaminants

Chapter 2. Boundary and/or thin-film lubrication, liquids and grease
  1. Physical and chemical absorption (discuss surface finish and similar influencing variables; oiliness or wetability)
  2. Chemical reaction
  3. E.P. concepts

Chapter 3. Full-film friction or lubrication—liquids
  1. Viscosity
  2. Hydrodynamic
  3. Hydrostatic
  4. Compressibility
  5. Turbulence, eddies
  6. Energy balance
  7. Inertia effects
  8. Cavitation
  9. Transient conditions
  10. Instability whip

Chapter 4. Full-film friction or lubrication, greases

Chapter 5. Wear
  1. Abrasive
  2. Corrosive
  3. Adhesive
  4. Impact

      5. Fretting
      6. Fatigue
      7. Cavitation erosion
      8. Electrical pitting
      9. Fluid erosion

Chapter 6. Flow through orifices and piping

Section 2. Physical Systems

Chapter 7. Machine elements—kinematics and wear patterns
      1. Sliding
        a. Journal
        b. Slider
        c. Thrust
        d. Ways
        e. Seals
        f. Screws
        g. Pistons
      2. Rolling
        a. Ball
        b. Roller
      3. Elements using squeeze-film lubrication
      4. Deformation
        a. Cutting
        b. Grinding
        c. Drawing, forming, extruding
        d. Stamping
        e. Rolling
        f. Polishing
      5. Combination of above; gears, cams, etc.

Chapter 8. Materials
      1. Metals
      2. Nonmetals
      3. Combination—metals, nonmetals

Section 3. Lubricants

Chapter 9. Function
      1. Control friction
      2. Control wear
      3. Control temperature
      4. Control corrosion
      5. Insulation (electrical)
      6. Power transmission
      7. Dampen shock (dashpots, gears)

Chapter 10. Types—both natural and synthetic
    1. Solids
       a. Elements
       b. Compounds
       c. Mixtures
    2. Liquids, natural
       a. Compounds
       b. Solutions
       c. Mixtures
    3. Liquids, synthetic
    4. Greases
    5. Gases
    6. Combination
       a. Solid-liquid
       b. Liquid-gases

Chapter 11. Properties (see ASLE "Phys Prop of Lube" as guide
    —include physical and chemical properties)
    Liquids and greases
    1. Viscosity
       a. Thermal variation
       b. Pressure variation
       c. Time variation
       d. Newtonian
       e. Non-Newtonian pumpability
       f. Shear stability
    2. Compressibility
    3. Conductivity: thermal and electrical
    4. Surface tension
    5. Density
    6. Oiliness, wetability
    Solid lubricants

Chapter 12. Performance (including bench tests, machine or functional tests, service evaluation)
    1. Film strength
       Falex, Timken, SAE, Almen, 4-ball, Ryder,
       Navy gear, etc.
    2. Engine
    3. Service life
    4. Oiliness: slip-stick tests
    5. Thermal stability
    6. Oxidation stability

Section 3. Chemical
Section 4. Pulp and paper
Section 5. Textiles
Section 6. Railroad
Section 7. Automotive fleets
Section 8. Power plants
Section 9. Mining
Section 10. Food processing
Section 11. Aircraft

Appendix

1. Glossary of terms
2. Symbols and nomenclature
3. Common basic formulas
4. Handy charts
5. Great men in lubrication: a summarized version of the LUBRI-CATION ENGINEERING series without photos.

GET YOURSELF UNDER CONTRACT

Once you are satisfied that your outline is satisfactory, the next step toward publication of your book is to secure a contract from the publisher of your choice. The contract, also called a Memorandum of Agreement, is a document drawn up between publisher and author. What the document does essentially is to set up a partnership between the author and the publisher.

By the terms of the contract, you as author agree to supply a complete manuscript that is technically accurate and in good physical condition. Most contracts for technical books do not set a date when you must deliver your manuscript. But many publishers like to receive the manuscript within about one year after the contract is signed.

The publisher, as one of the two partners to the agreement, promises to manufacture your manuscript in book form, to promote the book through his normal distribution facilities, and to pay you royalties on all copies that are sold. So the contract adds up to this partnership: You supply your technical know-how and the completed manuscript, along with the illustrations to be used in the book. Also, you secure all necessary permissions for use of copyrighted material that appears in the book. The publisher, on his side, supplies the manufacturing facilities, editing skill, design talent, sales facilities, and the financial investment required to produce and market your book. No financial investment of any kind is necessary on your part if your book is published by a reputable publisher. Of course, the publisher cannot assume any of the costs that you incur in the preparation of your manuscript. These costs include items like typing, securing illustrations, travel to sites important to your book, etc.

The advantage to you of being under contract is that you are assured that your book will be published if it is of suitable quality. Never attempt to write an entire technical book without first getting yourself under contract to a suitable publisher. For after you get the entire book written you may find that it is unpublishable. Or you may find that extensive revisions are necessary before publication is possible. So every experienced technical writer gets himself under contract just as soon as he can after he conceives of an idea for a book. How do you get a contract? Let's see.

Most book publishers today require three items from you before they will consider your project. These are: (1) a detailed outline of each chapter in the book, as well as an over-all outline covering all the chapters in the book, (2) two chapters in finished form as they will appear in the book, and (3) a preface in which you tell whom you have written the book for, why you have written the book, and what the reader will get from the book. With this material in hand the publisher can go about making his decision as to whether he wishes to go ahead with your project. If he decides to publish your book he will immediately offer you a contract.

If you are really serious about writing your book, you will make the three items listed above as good as you possibly can. For usually it is upon these that your project will either stand or fall. If your outline is poorly organized, if your chapters are hurriedly written, or if your preface rambles, your book does not have a very good chance of acceptance. So take every precaution possible to do as good a job as you can on this sample material.

Make your outlines as logical as possible, and see that they include every essential entry. Write your two sample chapters with utmost care. Include all the illustrations you intend to use in these chapters in the book. For your samples choose, say, Chapters 1 and 10 rather than Chapters 1 and 2. Or you could choose Chapter 2 and some later chapter, say 8 or 10 or 15. See that your preface states adequately why you are writing your book. If you cannot express the reasons for writing your book, examine your thinking once again. For if you cannot tell the publisher why you are writing the book there is really little reason for him to invest thousands of dollars in producing it.

Once again, you can see that writing a technical book is not a simple task. It involves the expenditure of a great deal of time and energy on your part. Since there is little point to wasting time, you should be completely certain that you have a genuine desire to write the book and the necessary talent to complete the project. If you find that you do not have these requirements it is best to discard the idea early. For if you do not, you may find the entire experience a disheartening one.

Your outline gives the publisher the scope and organization of your book. The completed sample chapters show him how well you can express yourself about your subject. They also indicate to the publisher the level of the audience you are aiming at. The preface tells whom you've written the book for, why you've written it, and what your readers will get from the book.

Once the publisher receives your sample material he sends it to outside critics and reviewers to analyze the material and to suggest how it can be improved, if this should be necessary. Suggestions that reviewers make are usually aimed at making your book more understandable or at tailoring it for a broader audience.

The publisher's decision on your book is based on the opinions of the reviewers and on his own study of the market and the manuscript. If his decision is favorable he will enter into an agreement with you to publish your book. He will offer you his contract which you sign, retaining a copy for yourself and returning one to him. The terms of typical book contracts are outlined in Chapter 1. Review these terms now.

Once the publisher agrees to publish your book, and sometimes even before, he will assign an editor to work with you. The editor stands ready to advise, help, cajole, or humor you, according to your needs. Since the book editor is usually a person with long experience in his field, he can be of major assistance to you. For besides answering questions on manuscript preparation, copyright laws, illustration sizes, and hundreds of other routine matters, the editor can advise you on the broader aspects of your task. Thus, if your outline needs some changes, if you wish to have an unbiased review of your ideas or manuscript, or if you need some helpful encouragement, the editor is ready to come to your assistance.

Behind every book published there is at least one author and one editor. The closeness of their association varies. Some authors must be led by the hand. Others are heard from by their editors only twice—once when the book is proposed and contracted for, and once when the manuscript is delivered. But regardless of the amount of attention or help you need, the editor will always be a sympathetic and understanding friend.

After an editor has been assigned to you and you have signed your contract with the publisher, you proceed to finish your manuscript. While working on your manuscript you can keep in touch with your editor, telling him of your progress. If any questions arise on the handling of your material he is ready to answer them.

On completion of your manuscript you submit it to your editor. The manuscript is again reviewed and a report is prepared for you. When you read it you may wonder why the reviewer didn't write the book himself instead of making unflattering comments and remarks about the manuscript. But you will find when you reach this stage in your book writing that most outside appraisal is usually constructive. The comments will call your attention to points that may be troublesome to your readers. If necessary, you may be asked to revise your manuscript to bring it into line with the reviewer's suggestions.

The procedure given in this chapter for outlining a book can be used for any type of technical book. In addition to the seven types listed in the previous chapter, which are probably the more familiar ones to you, many technical writers today author company books and industry-sponsored manuals. While both these types can be outlined as we have discussed in this chapter, you will find that there are certain differences, because not all the requirements of a regular commercial publisher must be met. But these differences are usually minor. When writing a book that is sponsored by a company or industry you will find that the nearer you can make the book approach a standard type the better reception it will have. And since all sponsored books are written for the largest distribution possible, you should make every effort to have the text and illustrations conform to what the technical reading public wants.

SUMMARY

Book ideas develop slowly. It may take many months or even years to develop the ideas for an outstanding technical book. Most technical books are written because none exist covering a certain phase of a field or the existing books in a field are outdated. Many books have their start as a series of articles, a series of lectures, a technical paper, catalog, report, or bulletin. To develop a book idea you must consider what type of book you want to write. Then you should study typical examples of published books of this type. Before writing your book you must prepare an outline for it. The outline should cover all the chapters in the book. As many entries as possible should be included in the outline. It is often advisable and helpful to divide a book into parts. These help both the reader and the author. Once you seriously decide to write a book you should prepare sample material for the publisher. Submit this to the publisher. If he decides to publish your book he will offer you a contract. If his terms are within the general ranges given in Chapter 1, sign the contract. If you desire, you can get some legal advice on the contract, but this is usually unnecessary with recognized technical-book publishers.

CHAPTER CHECK-UP

1. Do book ideas develop slowly or quickly? How long may it take to develop book ideas?
2. Name two common reasons for an author deciding to write a book.
3. What are other typical sources of book ideas?
4. What is the first step you should take after getting an idea for a book?
5. Where can you get hints on how typical technical books are arranged and illustrated?
6. What should you observe when studying typical technical books? Is it necessary for you to study the technical content of the books you look over?
7. What should you do when you find an author you admire?
8. Should you outline your book? If so, why?

9. Construct a typical outline for a book of your choice. Explain why you have used the subheads you chose.
10. Explain the difference between an over-all chapter outline and an individual chapter outline.
11. What kind of sample material should you prepare for a publisher? List the three items that every publisher requires.
12. Of what quality should the sample material be?
13. Why should you be under contract to a publisher?
14. What can the editor assigned to you do for you?

Chapter 17

WRITING AND ILLUSTRATING THE TECHNICAL BOOK

Once a publisher has put you under contract to write your book, you are ready to begin the long journey between the sample material and the finished manuscript. Right at the start you should recognize that writing a book is not a simple task. But if you approach it with the right attitude of mind and apply some of the hints given in this chapter, you will find the task somewhat easier. All the remarks in this chapter are useful for any type of technical book. So study them well because they will save you much misery and pain.

Before starting to write, review your outline. It will probably have been in the publisher's hands for some time. And if you have not looked at it during this time you will have a fresh approach when you see it again. Try to be very critical while you look it over. If any questions occur to you, note them immediately in the margin of the outline. Go through the entire outline quickly, marking down any thoughts that come to mind. Then once again go over the entire outline, this time slowly. Make your evaluation as objective as possible.

Make any changes that you find necessary. When the outline appears satisfactory, you are ready to proceed with your writing.

TWO IMPORTANT STEPS BEFORE YOU WRITE

With a good outline and a great deal of enthusiasm you need only two other tools before you start writing. These are: (1) a writing schedule, and (2) a progress notebook. Let's see what each of these is and how it will help you with your writing task.

Writing schedule. Trying to write a book without a schedule is much like taking a long trip without a timetable. You have no idea where you will be on a given date. So if you try to check your progress after a few days or weeks, you have nothing to tell where you should be. A writing schedule will relieve you of wasting time trying to figure where you should be.

To set up a writing schedule, study your outline. You already have two chapters completed. So subtract the number two from the total number of chapters in the book. Say that you plan to have twelve chapters. Subtracting two leaves ten. If you assume that it will take you one month to write each chapter the total writing time will be ten months. But one of your chapters may be a lot longer than others. Plan on taking more than a month for this chapter; say two months. Then your total writing time will be eleven months.

Now if you have had a good deal of writing experience you will know how closely your ordinary writing approaches finished copy. If your rough draft requires only minor changes, then you can plan on another month or two for polishing the finished manuscript. But if you are relatively new to the technical writing business you should plan on a longer period for rewriting. Assume that you allow four months for rewriting the first draft. With these time intervals, the experienced writer as a rule will spend twelve to thirteen months on his manuscript, while the newer writer will spend fourteen to fifteen months on his.

But you say, "I do not know how long it will take me to write a chapter. What do I do then?" Well, since you don't know, you must make some assumptions. Guess at how long it will take you to write each chapter. Allow a shorter time for the chapters that cover the material you are most familiar with. Allot a longer period for the chapters needing research or other special work.

Do not allow a writing schedule to frighten you. The schedule is nothing more than a series of check points. If you write rapidly and beat the deadline for a given chapter, go right ahead to the next one. The main purpose of a writing schedule is to help you see your way to the end of the project. If you try to write a book without a writing schedule you may find that somewhere near the middle you begin to lose enthusiasm. This is because you feel you have done a great deal of work and the end of your task is still far off in the future. But with a writing schedule, when you reach the middle of your book you will know that the end is only a few months away. This thought will act as an incentive to you to push ahead to that magical last chapter.

Don't underestimate the value of a writing schedule. It will keep you moving ahead toward the completion of your book. And it will add to your sense of accomplishment as you finish each chapter. You can even play a little game with yourself. If in comparing the actual amount of writing time you require with your scheduled time you find yourself ahead, you can imagine yourself as picking up days or weeks. This will allow more time for polishing your manuscript.

A schedule also helps you direct your energy output. As Fig. 17-1 shows, a schedule keeps your writing effort at a high level throughout the writing period. This means that you will waste less time worrying about meeting the final deadline.

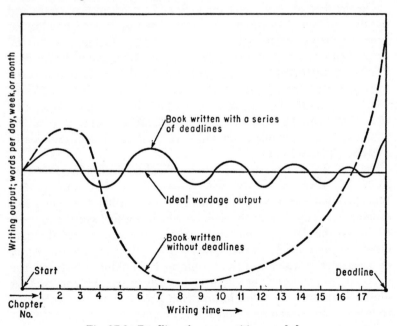

Fig. 17-1. Deadlines for your writing can help.

Another advantage of a writing schedule is that it helps you deliver your manuscript on time to the publisher. Since publishers have to plan well ahead of time on the books they will publish in the future, they are very appreciative when an author delivers his manuscript on the promised date. When you come around with another book the publisher will recall how promptly you met your deadline. This will incline him to regard your next project favorably. So do not start writing until you have prepared a realistic schedule.

Use a progress notebook. Writing a technical book is a full-time mental activity. You will find that you think of your book throughout your working day, and into the evening. During this time many thoughts will occur to you about the book, some of them extremely valuable. Unless you make a note of them immediately you may never be able to recall them.

Get yourself a 3- by 6-inch notebook that you can carry with you at all times. Number the pages in the notebook from the beginning to the end.

On the first page of your notebook make a list of the names and numbers of the chapters of your book. On the next page enter the time schedule you have set up for your writing. Include the specific date when you expect to finish each chapter. Next, enter the heading "Titles." On this page you can enter any good title ideas that occur to you. If you are a typical author you will start with one title for your book and by the time you are finished you will have thought of at least twelve others. Enter each of these on this page so when the final choice must be made you will have a list of the good candidates as well as the bad ones.

Devote the next few pages of your notebook to the heading "General Data." In these pages you will enter assorted facts and general thoughts that occur to you while you are writing the book. For example you might enter the date on which you first got the idea for the book, the date on which you signed the contract, and the date on which you started to write. Other entries might include the names of magazines in which you think your book should be advertised, the names of companies or people who could help you with research or illustrations, and any other information pertinent to the writing of your book and to its production and marketing.

The next heading in your notebook should be "Preface." Assign a few pages to it. In these pages make notes of information to be included in the preface of your book. List the names of people whom you wish to thank or otherwise acknowledge. If there are a great many acknowledgments to be made, you may find it advisable to set up a special "Credits" page in your notebook. Then there will be no chance of your overlooking an important person or firm when you come to write your preface. All this may sound unnecessary, but you will be amazed at how easy it is to overlook an important credit. With this special page for credits in your notebook you can enter all the credits you want to remember as they occur to you and they will be there to be readily picked out when you need them.

Skip a few pages and make the next entry in your notebook. This will be "Chapter 1." Skip a few more pages and enter "Chapter 2." Proceed this way until you have listed all the chapters in your book. Leave four to six pages for each chapter.

Now go back to Chapter 1 in your notebook and enter the outline for this chapter. Also enter any special thoughts you may have concerning Chapter 1. Do the same for all the other chapters in your book. You will now have in easy-to-use form a complete outline of your book, as well as a place to enter any thoughts you may have concerning any part of it.

Now as you go about your business, attend meetings, ride trains or planes, or do anything else, you have an easy way of recording every thought that comes to you about your book during the moments when your mind is free. Write these thoughts in your notebook as soon as they occur to you. For instance, if you learn that a certain firm would be an excellent source of an illustration for Chapter 8, make a note of this on the page devoted to that chapter. Or if you find that a slight change in the outline of Chapter 8 is necessary, make the change at once. Don't wait until the evening or some other time. You will probably have forgotten the thought by then and you will waste time trying to recover it.

The whole idea of this notebook is based on the enormous amount of work and thinking you will do in producing your technical book. If you can keep your manuscript under control at all times your writing will benefit and you will not have to work as hard as if you let your energy scatter. So don't ever try to write a technical book without the aid of a progress notebook and a writing schedule. These two tools can mean the difference between an outstanding book easily prepared and a poor one that took twice as much time as necessary. With your schedule and notebook set up you are ready to begin the serious task of writing your book. Let's see how you can do this without wasting time and energy.

WRITE, WRITE, WRITE

The only way to write your book is to put it into the form of words. And the only way to get the words on paper is by writing. Use a typewriter, a pen, or a pencil. But write.

Try to estimate how many words there will be in your book. Let's say that you find you will have about 60,000 words in the book. Set up a word schedule for each day. If you are an experienced writer you may be able to produce 1,000 words a day. As a beginner, 500 words may be your limit. But no matter which class you are in, decide how many words you will write each day you work on the book. Then try to meet the goal you have set up.

When you sit down to write, don't worry about the quality of your English. Just be sure of two things: (1) that your technical facts are completely accurate and (2) that you meet your wordage goal for that day. With accurate facts and a steady progression toward completion of your manuscript, you will find that your writing improves as you go along. If you worry and fret about verbs, nouns, infinitives, and other grammatical stumbling blocks, you will slow your writing. Then you may fall behind your over-all schedule, and this can lead to discouragement and a loss of enthusiasm.

As the pile of completed manuscript pages rises, your enthusiasm and interest will grow. So write and write. Remember that if your technical facts are accurate and you have a good subject, you can always have a specialist in English rewrite your manuscript if your English is extremely poor. Your main contributions in any technical book are the facts you present and the manner in which you present them. So get your facts straight. Then write a little each day.

You need not necessarily start writing with Chapter 1. If Chapter 6 is the easiest one in the book for you to do, start with it. For the more chapters you complete early in your schedule the easier the book will be. Many writers experience a letdown somewhere near the middle of their work. This is less apt to occur if the first half of the book has been easy going as the result of tackling the familiar chapters first. Or at least the letdown will not be serious. Another advantage of starting with the easier chapters is that it gives you more time to think over the difficult chapters. While you are thinking about the tough chapters you will probably get some useful ideas. Enter these in your notebook and they will be waiting for you when you reach the chapters you've been sidestepping.

Use headings. Headings are used in technical books, textbooks, and handbooks as a convenience to the reader. They point up the main theme and outline the development of thought.

You will note that in this book two forms of headings predominate. The one in small caps, flush left, on a separate line, divides the chapter into its main sections. An example is the WRITE, WRITE, WRITE which appears above. The second type of heading we use is the run-in italicized word or words at the beginning of some paragraphs. As you have gathered, the italicized words are subheads under the main headings dividing the chapter into sections. You, of course, need not use the same scheme. Choose a scheme that fits your book.

You can follow a main heading with a subhead, and this in turn may be followed by subsidiary headings. For the sake of clarity and smooth reading, restrict yourself to two or at the most three values of headings; too many guideposts may cause your reader to lose sight of the main thought in the chapter. And in the interests of attractive design, try to avoid a heading at the start of a chapter where it will follow directly below the chapter title and create an awkward space above the text.

Use center headings for major chapter breaks, and for "Problems," "Bibliography," etc. The prevailing head throughout the book should be a side head. When typing your manuscript, follow a consistent style of indicating the value of the headings, as shown in Fig. 17-2.

It is extremely important that you make the relative values of your headings clear. For if the headings are marked for type incorrectly by the publisher's copy editor, considerable resetting may be required later. When a heading printed on a separate line is changed in the galley proof to be run in at the beginning of a paragraph, usually the whole paragraph has to be reset. If you have any questions about the proper setup for headings, list all the headings in outline form for the guidance of the copy editor.

MAIN HEADING: CAPITALIZED AND CENTERED

Subheading: Separate-line, Flush with Margin, Underlined, Main
Words Capitalized

Subsidiary Heading: Paragraphed, Underlined, Main Words
Capitalized. The text follows in the same paragraph.

Fig. 17-2. Use consistent headings throughout your book. (*Courtesy of McGraw-Hill Book Co., Inc.*)

Although the numbering of headings may look needlessly precise, it is helpful in textbooks, advanced technical material, and in handbooks. Use either consecutive numbers throughout the book or double numbers by chapter, giving the chapter number first, for example, Section 3-6 for the sixth section in Chapter 3. Double numbering of headings, tables, illustrations, equations, etc., is recommended for textbooks and reference books because it simplifies cross reference and reduces the amount of renumbering when a revised edition is prepared. Handbooks are almost always double-numbered because they are frequently revised, and this system make the revision easier. Do not use complicated numbering systems with triple or quadruple numbers. They are cumbersome and are likely to be confusing to the average reader.

Give enough thought to your headings and subheads to make them suitable for your particular book. Well-organized headings can help your thinking and can make your book much easier for the reader to use. So the time you spend developing headings is well worth while.

Chapters. A chapter should cover an important phase of your subject. It should have unity within itself. To achieve unity within a chapter you should limit its content to exactly what is covered by the chapter heading. For instance if the name of your chapter is "Centrifugal Pumps" do not include any other types of pumps, except as they are related to centrifugal pumps. (And when referring to other types be sure to state how centrifugal pumps are related to the others; not how the others are related to centrifugal pumps.) In a chapter dealing with an elementary phase of your subject do not bring in advanced concepts, except to refer to them if they are covered in a later chapter.

By planning your chapters so that each is a well-organized unit you make your writing task easier. While writing any given chapter you can forget about the others since you know that they will adequately cover their subject matter.

How long should a chapter be? Only you can answer this question for your book. There are no fixed rules. But if you study a number of technical books you will find that relatively few contain chapters that are less than two pages long. This is because you seldom find a phase of a technical subject that can be covered in two printed pages.

If you can possibly do so, arrange to have a short chapter followed by a longer one. More important, try to follow a long chapter with a shorter one. This arrangement of your subject matter will make your book more appealing to readers. Many readers become bored with a book when they find that it has a repetitious pattern of chapter length. By following a long chapter with a short one you give the reader a sense of accomplishment when he finishes the short one in a smaller interval of time.

In an illustrated technical book you will find that you can use your photographs and drawings to vary the chapter pattern. Thus in a chapter that is illustrated mostly with photographs the reader may begin to wonder what the interior or hookup of the illustrated devices looks like. Perhaps you can satisfy his curiosity in the next chapter by using a number of line drawings showing these details. In this way the reader obtains a clearer concept of the subject and his interest is maintained at a higher level.

As in all other types of writing, you must think of your reader first when planning your chapters. For remember that although writing your book may give you a great deal of pleasure, you are still writing it to be read by others. So avoid trick schemes when planning your chapters. Instead aim at the utmost clarity you can achieve. Only when you strive constantly for clarity will you feel that you have done your best for the reader. After all, if you don't do your best you might as well not write the book. Never forget that the easier your book is to understand and use, the more readers and appreciation it will attract.

Work your illustrations. Make your illustrations carry their share of the load. Never use an illustration just because it is pretty or it appeals to you. Choose and use only those illustrations that show your reader an important point.

Try to refer to every illustration in your text. Nothing confuses a reader more than to see some illustrations in a book without any reference in the text. Since the caption or legend for an illustration must be relatively short, you generally must include some additional data about the illustration in the text of your book. If you do not have any references in your text to the illustrations the reader is at a loss as to just how he should relate the illustrations to what he reads in the text.

By referring to your illustrations in your text you not only make the illustrations carry their share of the load but add to the unity of your book, because all the elements are neatly tied together. Your reader will show his appreciation by using your book more than one that is poorly put together.

Every time you choose an illustration remember that the making and handling of illustrations greatly increase the manufacturing costs of your book. These, in turn, increase the price of your book. So before deciding to include an illustration ask yourself: *Is this illustration necessary?* If the answer is yes, then include the illustration in your book. But if you are at all in doubt about the value of the illustration put it aside and think further about it. Eliminate illustrations that do not appear absolutely necessary for the understanding of your subject matter.

In considering each illustration, ask yourself the following questions:

1. Is it informative? Does it enhance or clarify the text?
2. Is it pertinent to a main theme or merely to a side issue?
3. Is it appropriate in period, content, and style to the text it illustrates?
4. Is it clear, interesting, up-to-date?
5. Does it duplicate some other illustrations you have chosen? Or does it illustrate something you have described so graphically that the reader can visualize it without seeing an illustration?
6. Is it of good quality for reproduction?
7. Can it be reduced to page size or smaller and still be clear?

8. Can it be set vertically on the page so the reader will not have to turn the book to look at it?

9. Does it include unnecessary details or areas? If so, could it be made more pertinent by cropping or retouching?

By applying these questions to each illustration you can determine if it is suitable for your book. To find exactly how the publisher wants you to submit illustrations, contact your editor. He will have specific instructions as to how you should submit drawings and photographs. Follow these instructions exactly. For in doing exactly as the publisher requests you save him time and money. Your book will probably be published sooner and its price will be lower than if you make your own rules as you go along.

Captions. Number your captions, or legends, to correspond to the illustrations. Submit two copies of the captions, typed double spaced in list form. Make your captions concise and pertinent; do not use the captions as a catch-all for information you have neglected to supply in the text. Be sure that your captions follow the style of your manuscript, rather than the varying styles of the sources from which you secured them. Figure 17-3 shows several different arrangements for typing illustration captions.

Numbering illustrations. Either number your illustrations consecutively throughout the book or double-number them by chapter. Refer to your illustrations in the text by figure number, not by page number. Correct page numbers cannot be supplied until all the pages have been made up by the printer.

Double-numbering is preferred by many publishers today, and most technical books use this system. It means that you refer to your illustrations with two numbers. The first number is the chapter number. It is followed by a hyphen and a second number, denoting the number of the illustration within the chapter. For example, Fig. 3-5 refers to the fifth illustration in Chapter 3. The double-numbering system has the advantage that if you add or delete illustrations you need change the illustration numbers and references only within the chapter. Also, it is easier to insert new illustrations when you are revising your book at a later date.

Finding illustrations. You can obtain illustrations from the public-relations department of business and industrial firms, from govern-

Fig. 3-5. Diagrammatic representation of concept formation.
(From D. M. Johnson, Essentials of Psychology,
McGraw-Hill Book Company, Inc., New York, 1948.
By permission of the publishers.)

Fig. 4-5. Atlas vertebra of cat: A, dorsal view; B, ante-
rior view. (Drawn by James Brown.)

Trend of newspaper and magazine advertising in 52 cities by
five major classifications, 1928 to 1946. (Figures from
Media Records, Inc.)

Fig. 226. A sea slug, Navanax inermis. X 1/2. (Courtesy of
Dr. and Mrs. F. M. MacFarland.)

Fig. 350. Arrangement of stones in section of Notre Dame at
Dijon. (After Viollet-le-Duc.)

Fig. 17-3. Typical legends for books. (*Courtesy of McGraw-Hill Book Co., Inc.*)

ment agencies, service organizations, libraries, schools, museums, commercial photographers, and publishers of periodicals and books. Ink drawings and glossy photographic prints or halftones usually give best results in the printed book.

The printed page of a book or magazine can sometimes be used as copy for a line cut; but it will not reproduce as well as original copy. Never use a printed halftone as copy to make another halftone, for a second pattern of black dots will be superimposed on the previous one and the result will be a cross pattern, making an unattractive illustration.

You must secure permission in writing for the use of illustrations from any source, whether they are reproduced exactly or modified. Include credit to the source of the illustration in the caption of the illustration. If the wording of the credit is specified by the source, call this to the attention of your publisher.

If you take an illustration directly from another book, introduce the caption for this illustration by "From." If you redraw an illustration from another book use the word "After." But if you base a new illustration on an existing illustration in a book use the words "Adapted from."

Summaries. You can help your reader by giving a summary at the end of each chapter. You need not use more than one or two paragraphs to do this. Write your summary by going through the entire chapter and picking out the key thoughts. Include only these in your summary. Never try to rewrite the chapter in your summary. You will only bore your reader and waste his time.

Problems or questions. Include problems or questions at the end of your chapters if your material is such that your readers will benefit from solving problems or answering questions. Once again *you* must decide if problems or questions should be included in your book. As you know, most textbooks have either problems or questions, or both. Probably the only type of modern technical book that does not include either problems or questions is the handbook. We shall discuss the handbook in greater detail later in this chapter.

If you include problems in your book be sure to solve them and check each solution several times before inserting it in your manuscript. If your book is a college text you may want to omit the answers to problems. Or you may wish to include only every other answer. You would be wise to follow the recommendations of your publisher in this matter.

Answers to questions require more space and are generally not included. But if you wish to include some of the answers to the questions try to reduce the answers to their essentials. Again, the decision rests with you. If you are in doubt, check with your editor to find out what the publisher's policy is.

HANDBOOKS

A handbook is a documented volume of proven facts written in a practical, concise form. It comprehensively covers a broad subject area. The handbook is the basic, authoritative reference work for the practicing engineer, scientist, technician, and student.

There are definite basic differences between a handbook and a textbook. A textbook deals with rudiments, reasoning, theory, problems, and mathematical concepts. It usually contains only enough practical treatment to clinch the theory. A handbook contains working information, and only enough theory to explain basic practice. The handbook condenses theory and hypotheses to ultimate terseness to give more space to compiled data and tables designed to meet the needs of the engineer and scientist.

If you take on the job of being the editor of a handbook your best course to follow is to work closely with the editor assigned to you by the publisher. Your editor will probably have had long experience in this field and he can advise you on how most efficiently to produce the book.

In editing a handbook your biggest task is not writing—rather it is the selection of suitable contributors. The ideal contributor is a person who has achieved some prominence in his sphere. He has probably written technical papers on his speciality and may have written articles for technical magazines. Often he is the author of a book dealing with his particular field. And he is usually an active worker on committees of technical or engineering societies. You may find this type of contributor working in industry or in a research laboratory or teaching in a college or university.

Another type of contributor not to be overlooked is the man who is a level or two below the top men in his field. He probably is not known outside of his chosen area but is considered by his associates and those working in the field as a person with demonstrated ability and future promise.

Experience shows that men of both types are quite willing to contribute to handbooks, whereas they might not write for another type of publication. As editor-in-chief your initial approach to your contributors will be in person, by telephone, or by letter. In your first contact with a prospective contributor explain the scope of the handbook, the reasons for its preparation, and the fact that the handbook has been placed under contract by a recognized publisher. You should also indicate the name and scope of the section you would like the contributor to write, and the tentative deadline for his manuscript.

Your first letter to a prospective contributor is merely an exploratory one, opening the way for more detailed correspondence later. If your publisher has had much previous experience with handbooks he will probably be able to supply you with typical letters you can use as a guide in preparing your own. Examine the sample letters carefully and then write your own. It is not desirable in your first letter to include a copy of the entire outline of the handbook, or mention the honorarium you expect to pay.

The follow-up letter must be tailored to fit the particular situation. In the follow-up letter acknowledging the acceptance of the writing assignment by the contributor you give additional information and specific instructions to guide him in preparing his manuscript. Other types of letters are used to follow-up a tentative acceptance or a weak refusal. At this stage of your project it is well for you to keep in close contact with your publisher. Often a letter or call from the publisher to a prospective contributor is extremely helpful.

It is extremely important that you keep in touch with each contributor as he develops his section. It is wise for you to work with the publisher's handbook editor in setting up a series of letters covering the entire production of the handbook. You should set up these letters at the time the first invitations to potential contributors are issued. If you set up a basic set of letters in advance you can use them as needed, with appropriate modifications.

A typical series of letters might include the following: (1) invitation to potential contributor to write a section, (2) follow-up letter to potential contributor invited by telephone or in person, (3) follow-up letter to contributor accepting your original invitation, (4) follow-up letter to weak refusal or tentative acceptance, (5) acknowledgment and instructions to those agreeing to become contributors to your handbook (this should be done by both the editor-in-chief and publisher), (6) a series of letters at regular intervals giving each contributor the names of other contributors, special information, progress reports, etc., (7) notification of approaching deadline—one month in advance, (8) acknowledgment of the manuscript, (9) a follow-up letter two weeks after the manuscript is due if it has not been received (discuss overdue manuscripts as soon as possible with your publisher so that a suitable course of action can be taken to expedite the manuscripts), (10) return of manuscript to the contributor after it has been reviewed if further work is needed on it.

It is very important that you as editor-in-chief set up some system for keeping track of the status of each contributor's manuscript: when follow-ups should be made, deadlines, etc. Some handbook editors prefer to use index cards with a card for each contributor; others find it more practical to use a loose-leaf notebook and assign a page to each contributor. Still others find that a large wall chart gives them the information they need at a glance.

Contributors' compensation. Handbook contributors are paid by you as editor-in-chief of the handbook. The compensation is in the form of a cash payment, an honorarium, as well as a complimentary copy of the handbook. The budget for these payments is discussed and worked out with the handbook editor of the publisher in advance of contacting possible contributors. Usually the publisher advances funds for these payments, against the editor-in-chief's future royalties. In certain cases the publisher may advance funds for stenographic and editorial help.

Because of the number and caliber of the contributors involved in a major handbook, it is economically impossible to pay each a sufficient sum to compensate him for the time, effort, and experience he gives to the project. Obviously, then, there must be a stronger reason than the money involved to make contributors willing to give their time and effort to write sections for a handbook. Long experience in developing handbooks shows that contributors are motivated chiefly by the following factors:

The top-flight man will contribute a section for the simple reason that if he does not become associated with the project he will be conspicuous by his absence. If the book is a basic handbook and there is every reason to believe that it may become the bible in its field, this alone will attract many top-flight contributors. Another reason that you should not overlook is that the handbook gives the leaders in any field a good opportunity to make a lasting contribution to the literature of their fields. To the man on his way up the biggest lure is that the handbook, by bracketing him with the top names in his field, could well be the means to more prestige, a better job, more pay, etc. That this is sound reasoning has been proved time and time again.

Information for contributors. With the contributor's acceptance in hand, the editor-in-chief should furnish him with detailed information on how to proceed with the actual writing of his section. At this point it is well to stress again to the contributor the objectives of the handbook, its potential audience, and the basic underlying philosophy behind it. The contributor should be given an over-all outline of the entire handbook so that he may see how his section fits into the picture. He should also be given a skeleton outline of his section with an invitation to suggest improvements in it.

The editor-in-chief should emphasize to his contributors the following general points that should guide them in preparing their individual manuscripts: general descriptive matter and information, history of the art and its development, and like material should be condensed to the shortest possible form without omitting essentials or sacrificing accuracy. In general, the fundamentals of engineering theory should be presented in the briefest form, but no reasoning or hypothesis should be included, nor the derivation of formulas. The last belongs to a textbook or treatise; a handbook should present results alone. In short, it is to be assumed that the biggest user of the handbook will be an engineer, scientist, or technician having some previous acquaintance with engineering or scientific theory and practice.

Point out to all contributors that in selecting data for use in the handbook, each contributor is expected to exercise critical judgment and choose only the best, and to sum up the results of experience to indicate what constitutes standard practice under typical conditions. When authorities differ as to what is preferred practice, the contributor should state the case fairly for both sides, regardless of his own opinion or convictions. In the case of unsettled controversies, or where a rapidly changing art has not yet evolved a dominant or ruling practice, conclusions should not be attempted but the case presented as it stands.

The physical preparation of the manuscript cannot be stressed too often by the editor-in-chief. The contributors must be told in exact detail just how many manuscript pages are expected and in what form they should be prepared. As editor-in-chief you must understand the importance of and assume the responsibility for proper manuscript preparation. A good manuscript will go through production more smoothly and save both the publisher and the editor-in-chief time and money in author's alterations. The publisher's editing staff will be able to read and mark the manuscript more accurately and the printer will therefore make fewer typesetting errors. If the manuscript is not acceptably prepared, the publisher will have the manuscript retyped at the editor-in-chief's expense. Each contributor should also be warned to keep a carbon of his manuscript.

All contributors should be given a firm date for submitting the first drafts of their sections. This is usually covered in the editor-in-chief's letter acknowledging the acceptance of a contributor to write a certain section. Three or four months is the usual time allowed for writing a section. Contributors are expected to get permission to use material copyrighted by other publications.

The manuscript. As the individual manuscripts are received, you should examine them for style, content, and length. Do as careful an editing job as possible. It is your responsibility to be sure that the manuscript covers the area assigned, is concisely written, and subscribes to the over-all philosophy of the book. While it is hoped that the contributors and editor-in-chief will give some thought to spelling, grammar, standard abbreviations, and mechanical details of this sort, it is not expected that a disproportionate amount of time be spent on this phase. The publisher's own copy editors will do the major part of this job. This, of course, is not meant to imply that they will or can rewrite any manuscript. It is the responsibility of the contributor and editor-in-chief to furnish a clearly written and understandable manuscript. The editor-in-chief must stress and see that each contributor conforms to the following so that the final manuscript submitted to the publisher is:

1. Typed on one side of the sheet. The ribbon copy should be submitted; carbon or ditto copy is unsatisfactory and must be retyped before it is submitted to the publisher.

2. Double spaced. This includes footnotes and bibliographies. Tear

sheets from other periodicals and copy printed on both sides of the sheet should not be submitted.

3. Numbered consecutively through its entirety or submitted by section with each section consecutively numbered.

4. Separated from the illustrations. Two copies of the legends or captions for the illustrations are necessary and should be submitted with the manuscript.

With a vigorous system of contributor communication and control, the average handbook manuscript can be completed and submitted to the publisher within fourteen to eighteen months.

Manuscript review. In addition to the editor-in-chief's review of the various sections, it is usually well to get a critical appraisal from another source. The publisher makes arrangements for this review using a staff of outside advisers. These reviews are usually obtained as each manuscript is received by the editor-in-chief, rather than when the complete manuscript is in hand. This section-by-section review permits any necessary rewriting, adding, or deleting of material without holding up the entire project once the entire handbook manuscript is completed and ready for production. If the editor-in-chief has any specific queries on any section, these can be sent on to the reviewers for their comments as well.

After the review, the manuscript is then sent back to the contributor for final polishing in line with the editor-in-chief's and reviewers' comments. (Under certain circumstances the editor-in-chief can make the necessary changes himself without returning the manuscript to the contributor.) A rigid deadline one month later is usually set for resubmitting the manuscript. In some cases the first draft can be considered the final draft. If a contributed section is not up to par and it would be embarrassing or difficult for the editor-in-chief to so inform the contributor, the publisher usually takes over this diplomatic assignment.

Illustrations. Most handbooks, because of their length, are printed on Bible stock, which does not take photographs clearly. For this reason it is urged that line cuts be used exclusively. It is hoped that contributors will furnish inked illustrations ready for reproduction, but if this is not possible, the publisher will have the illustrations redrawn from pencil sketches. Of course, these sketches should be clear enough to permit the draftsmen to work from them.

IT'S UP TO YOU

Use of the hints given in this chapter should be a big help in the writing of your book. The hints should also be of real value to you if you are editing a handbook. But you must remember that in the long run you, and only you, can write the book.

When you reach the last page of your manuscript you will probably find that you will have to reread the entire text at least once. While you are rereading the manuscript, change the wording here and there as necessary; check the illustrations against the text to see that your references are correct, and check all tables. Make every effort to see that your manuscript is in the best possible condition.

SUMMARY

Before you start to write your book, review your outline. Make any changes that appear necessary. Next set up a writing schedule and a progress notebook. Start writing your book, adhering as closely as possible to your schedule. As ideas for your book occur to you, enter them in your notebook. Use headings throughout your manuscript to assist your reader in understanding the flow of your thoughts. Be sure to plan your chapters carefully. Make your illustrations work with your text. Choose illustrations not because they are pretty but because they can carry a share of the instruction load. Make liberal use of summaries, problems, and questions, if you think any or all of these will be useful to your readers.

In editing a handbook you must carefully preplan its entire production. Also, you must work very closely with the publisher's handbook editor. Scheduling is extremely important in a handbook and you should never overlook it.

CHAPTER CHECK-UP

1. What is the first step you should take before starting to write your book?
2. Name two important aids to controlling the progress of your book. Set up a typical example of both these aids.
3. How should you go about setting up a writing schedule if you have never done this before?

4. What is a progress notebook? How should you use it?
5. Describe how you would set up the various sections of your progress notebook.
6. How many words should you plan on writing each day?
7. Should you worry about the quality of your English as you write?
8. What two items should you be most careful about while writing your book?
9. Is it necessary for you to start with Chapter 1 and write through to the last chapter? If not, what are the advantages of writing in another order?
10. What kinds of headings are used in technical books? What should your headings do for your reader?
11. How long should a chapter be? What is meant by unity in a chapter?
12. How can you make sure that your illustrations carry their share of the load?
13. What should you consider in selecting an illustration? List nine qualities you should look for in an illustration.
14. What are the important characteristics of captions?
15. List several ways of numbering your illustrations.
16. Where can you find good illustrations for your book? How can you secure permission to use an illustration?
17. List three aids to better understanding which you can use in your book. What must you keep in mind in using each of these aids?
18. What is the difference between a handbook and other types of technical books?
19. What kind of contributors can you secure for a handbook?
20. Describe the types of letters that it is necessary for an editor to write in the process of producing a handbook.
21. What kind of information should you supply to the contributors of your handbook?
22. Describe the review process for the sections of handbooks.

INDEX